Growing Up with SCIENCE®

Third Edition

3

Cable travel–Cotton

 **Marshall Cavendish**
Reference
New York

Marshall Cavendish
99 White Plains Road
Tarrytown, NY 10591

www.marshallcavendish.us

© 2006 Marshall Cavendish Corporation
© 1987, 1990 Marshall Cavendish Limited

GROWING UP WITH SCIENCE is a registered trademark
of Marshall Cavendish Corporation

Library of Congress Cataloging-in-Publication Data

Growing up with science.— 3rd ed.
     p. cm.
   Includes index.
   Contents: v. 1. Abrasive-Astronomy — v. 2. Atmosphere-Cable television —
v. 3. Cable travel-Cotton — v. 4. Crane-Electricity — v. 5 Electric motor-
Friction — v. 6. Fuel cell-Immune system — v. 7. Induction-Magnetism —
v. 8. Mapmaking-Mining and quarrying — v. 9. Missile and torpedo-Oil
exploration and refining — v. 10. Optics-Plant kingdom — v. 11. Plasma
physics-Radiotherapy — v. 12. Railroad system-Seismology — v. 13.
Semiconductor-Sports — v. 14. Spring-Thermography — v. 15. Thermometer-
Virus, biological — v. 16. Virus, computer-Zoology — v. 17. Index.
   ISBN 0-7614-7505-2 (set)
   ISBN 0-7614-7508-7 (vol. 3)
   1. Science—Encyclopedias.

Q121.G764 2006
503—dc22

                                              2004049962
                              09 08 07 06 05 6 5 4 3 2 1
Printed in China

CONSULTANT

Donald R. Franceschetti, Ph.D.
Dunavant Professor at the University of Memphis

Donald R. Franceschetti is a member of the American
Chemical Society, the American Physical Society, the
Cognitive Science Society, the History of Science Society,
and the Society for Neuroscience.

CONTRIBUTORS TO VOLUME 3

Kim Bryan   Tim Harris

Michael Burns   Rob Houston

Martin Clowes   Nathan Lepora

Simon Hall   Jim Martin

Marshall Cavendish

Editor: Peter Mavrikis

Editorial Director: Paul Bernabeo

Production Manager: Alan Tsai

The Brown Reference Group

Editors: Leon Gray and Simon Hall

Designer: Sarah Williams

Picture Researcher: Helen Simm

Indexer: Kay Ollerenshaw

Illustrators: Darren Awuah and Mark Walker

Managing Editor: Bridget Giles

Art Director: Dave Goodman

PICTURE CREDITS

Cover inset: National Aeronautics and Space Administration

Adobe Systems Incorporated: 369; **Anglo American plc:** 375; **Apple Computer, Inc.:** 272; **Ardea:** John Daniels 332; **Art I Need:** 292, 314; **The Brown Reference Group plc:** 325; **Michael Burns:** 362; **Compaq:** 361; **Corbis:** Paul Almasy 269, 294, Lester V. Bergman 277, 282, Bettmann 261, 287, Jonathan Blair 273, Sheldan Collins 278, Ed Eckstein 348 (*bottom*), Robert Gill/Papilio 298, Richard Gross 279, Charles Gupton 364, Jeremy Horner 377, Ted Horowitz 322, Dave G. Houser 350, Lester Lefkowitz 330, John Madere 308, Ludovic Maisant 357, Raoul Minsart 367, Gail Mooney 313, Sally A. Morgan/Ecoscene 348 (*top*), Roger Ressmeyer 268, Science Pictures Ltd. 335, Ted Spiegel 288, James A. Sugar 378, Russell Underwood 262 (*top*), Bill Varie 262 (*bottom*), Dennis Wilson 305, Jim Zukerman 300; **DaimlerChrysler:** 296, 311; **Digital Vision:** 286, 293, 295, 306, 319, 346, 354, 373; Discreet: 370 (*left*); **Dymag:** 291; **European Space Agency:** CNES/Arianspace-service Optique CSG, J. Huart 353; **Getty Images:** Hulton Archive 274, Image Bank 283; **Hemera Photo Objects:** 263, 356, 374, 376 (*bottom*); **Image State:** Didier Givois 299; **imagingbody.com:** 303, 328, 329; **Intel Corporation:** 360 (*bottom*); **Anthony Lambert:** 351; **Lawrence Livermore National Laboratory:** 363 (*bottom*); **Microsoft Corporation:** 363 (*top*), 365, 369 (*top right*); **NASA:** 289, 307, 309 (*top*), 355 (*right*); **National Library of Medicine:** 327; **New Line Cinema:** 371; **Newscast:** De Beers 284; **NOAA:** 344 (*right*), Carol Baldwin 345 (*left*), Ralph F. Kresge 345 (*right*), OAR/ERL/NSSL 344 (*left*); **Nobel Foundation:** 304 (*top*), 304 (*bottom*); **Photodisc:** 260, 265, 331, 334 (*top right*), 334 (*top left*), 334 (*bottom right*), 334 (*bottom left*), 334 (*center*), 358; **Photos12.com:** 368; **Rex Features:** 360 (*top left*); **Science Photo Library:** Martyn F. Chillmaia 315, Colin Cuthbert 323, Dr. Fred Espenak 312, Mauro Fermariello 366, Rosenfeld Images Ltd. 290, Charles D. Winters 317, 318; **Sony Computer Entertainment Europe:** 370 (*right*); **Sony Electronics Inc.:** 267, 270, 271; **Still Pictures:** A. Ishokon/UNEP 337, Pascal Kobeh 339; **Sylvia Cordaiy Picture Library:** 276; **Texas Instruments:** 264; **Topham Picturepoint:** British Library/HIP 320, Rachel Epstein/Imageworks 340, Chris Fitzgerald/Imageworks 343; **Travel Ink:** Derek Allen 310, Nigel Bown-Morris 275, Julian Parton 297, David Toase 376 (*top*); **University of Pennsylvania Library:** Smith Collection 266, 280, 321, 333, 372; **USDA/ARS:** Scott Bauer 281 (*top*), 341, Peggy Greb 381, Ken Hammond 281 (*top*), David Nance 380 (*top*), 379, Keith Weller 324; **U.S. Dept. of Defense:** 352, 359; **U.S. Library of Congress:** 380 (*bottom*)

CONTENTS

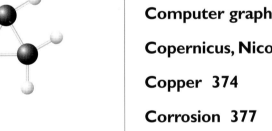

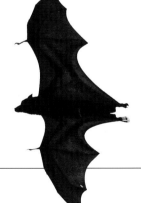

KEY TO COLOR CODING OF ARTICLES

■ EARTH, SPACE, AND ENVIRONMENTAL SCIENCES

■ LIFE SCIENCES AND MEDICINE

■ MATHEMATICS

■ PHYSICS AND CHEMISTRY

■ TECHNOLOGY

■ PEOPLE

Cable travel

A cable car is a vehicle that is pulled by a cable up and down a steep hill or mountain. Most cable cars have been replaced by more modern forms of transportation, but a few survive as important tourist attractions.

Cable railroads do not have locomotives to pull the cars. Instead, the cars are pulled by cable from an engine fixed at one end of the slope. Most cable railroads are funicular. Funicular railroads run on parallel tracks running up the slope. One track carries the car going up the slope, and the other carries the car coming down. The two cars are linked together by the pulling cable. This cable goes from one car, up and over a driving winch at the top, then down to the other car. When one car is at the top of the slope, the other is at the bottom.

As the car at the top of the slope begins to descend, the car at the bottom begins to ascend. The weight of the descending car helps pull up the ascending car. The engine therefore needs much less power than it would if it had to haul up the ascending car by itself.

Water-powered cable cars

Early funiculars had a simple power source. Each car carried a big water tank. The car at the top station carried a full tank of water. When it reached the bottom station, the tank was emptied. Since the descending car, carrying the full tank of water, was much heavier than the ascending car, no stationary engine was needed to power the arrangement.

Mountain railroads

The world's first funicular railroad is thought to have been built in Naples, Italy, in the late 1830s. The funicular crossed 5 miles (8 kilometers) from Naples to the royal residence in Portici. Most funiculars are used to negotiate very steep inclines,

▲ *The Duquesne Incline funicular railroad has served the residents of Duquesne Heights, Pittsburgh, since 1877. Two of the original cable cars still transport passengers up and down the steep incline.*

but they vary in steepness. On the gradual inclines the cars are very much the same as ordinary railroad cars. On steeper inclines, the cars have a number of separate compartments. These are graded one from another so that while the floors are level, a compartment at the higher end may be 10 or 15 feet (3 or 4 meters) higher than the lowest compartment at the other end.

Brake and safety systems are very important on steep mountain railroads. There are a number of brake systems to stop the car quickly in case the cable breaks accidentally. On very steep lines, ordinary disc brakes, such as those used in an automobile, would be ineffective. Instead, powerful grippers under the car clamp onto the track as soon as the cable becomes slack.

The hilly streets of San Francisco are home to a different kind of cable car. A continuous cable, driven by a stationary engine, runs in a slot between the rails. The driver starts and stops the cable car by gripping and releasing the moving cable in conjunction with the vehicle's brake system.

Aerial cable cars

Modern aerial cable cars are driven by electrically powered winding units. They are the most popular form of transportation in places where mountains attract summer tourists and winter sports enthusiasts. The aerial cable is much cheaper to build than the funicular. Switzerland now has the biggest mountain transport system in the world.

> ### DID YOU KNOW?
>
> The world's highest and longest aerial cable route can be found in Venezuela. It rises 10,250 feet (3,124 meters) from Mérida City to the summit of Pico Espejo. Three car changes are needed to travel the 8-mile (13-kilometer) journey.

There are three kinds of aerial cable cars. Large cars transport up to one hundred people and work rather like funicular railroads. There are usually two cars balancing each other. The cars may travel distances of up to 2 miles (3 kilometers). Open chairlifts have single or twin seats. A large number of chairs are spaced at intervals on the cable. They are seldom carried above 30 feet (9.5 meters) from the ground, and they may have runs of up to 2 miles (3 kilometers) or more. Most enclosed chairlifts carry four passengers. Like open chairlifts, they have many cars spaced along the cable, and they often operate at treetop height.

◀ *This photograph shows the western terminus of the California Street Cable Railroad in San Francisco. The photo was taken in 1883—ten years after English engineer Andrew Hallidie (1836–1900) built the first section of the railroad. San Francisco is now the only city in the world to operate street cable cars.*

◀ ***There is a winding wheel at the top and bottom of a T-bar ski lift. A traction cable passes around both winding wheels. T-bars are spaced evenly along the length of the cable. Two skiers sit on either side of one T-bar, and the cable carries them up the slope.***

Large cable cars have a gondola with some seats and space for people to stand. The gondola hangs from a truck that has a number of grooved pulley wheels. The wheels ride on carrying cables, which are anchored at both ends of the line. The carrying cables are supported along the run by steel pylons built up from the ground. The cars are powered by a traction cable attached to the top of the car. The traction cable forms a continuous loop, passing around winding wheels at both ends of the line. Engineers must work out the length of the traction cable to ensure the two cabins reach the opposite ends of the line at the same time.

Some of the big aerial cable lines have pylons spaced more than 1 mile (1.6 kilometers) apart. They may be as much as 1,000 feet (310 meters) above the ground when they are crossing valleys or rising up steep mountain faces.

Chairlifts are usually carried by single continuous cables that both support and pull the chairs. Some chairs are permanently attached to the cable, which runs without stopping. Passengers must get on and off at each end while the chair is slowly moving. An attendant is usually there to help them. Two-seat chairs are not usually permanently attached to the cable. They are attached to it by grippers, which can be released. At the start and end of the journey there are short lengths of rail that allow the chairs to run on and off the moving cable.

DID YOU KNOW?

The Wetterhorn Lift near Grindelwald, Switzerland, was the world's first aerial cable car. It opened in 1908 but was taken out of service when World War I broke out in 1914. All that remains are the upper station, which was renovated in the early 1990s, and the ruins of the lower station.

▲ ***Chairlifts are a comfortable way for skiers to reach the top of a slope. Most chairlifts consist of open chairs with seats for up to four passengers. Chairlifts can work over uneven ground because the passengers do not come into contact with the ground.***

See also: COG RAILROAD • MOUNTAIN

Calculator

Calculating machines, from the ancient abacus to the latest electronic pocket calculators, take the mental effort out of arithmetic. Calculators provide instant answers to math problems that might otherwise take a long time to figure out.

One of the oldest and simplest calculating machines is the abacus. The abacus has been in use for thousands of years, from before the development of the Hindu–Arabic number systems (around 600 BCE) on which modern numbers are based. Before this time, people did all counting, addition, and subtraction with an abacus. The ancient Greeks and Romans used pebbles or metal disks as counters, moving them on marked boards to work out problems. Later, the counters were strung on wires mounted in a frame. The user flipped the beads up and down to do calculations.

Slide rule

European developments in mathematics led to the invention of the slide rule by two English mathematicians, Edmund Gunter (1581–1626) and William Oughtred (1574–1660), during the early seventeenth century. Unlike the abacus, the slide rule allows the user to perform multiplication and division. Its use relies on the slightly earlier development of logarithms.

Logarithms (logs) are a mathematical system that defines any number in terms of the power to which a given base number has to be raised. In our ordinary counting system using the base of 10, for example, 100 equals 10 x 10, or 10^2, or 10 to the power of 2. The logarithm of 100 is, therefore, 2.

▶ **The abacus is one of the oldest adding machines. It is used for basic addition or subtraction by moving the disks up and down the wires. The disks against the center bar represent the numbers in use.**

Adding together the logs of two numbers is the same as multiplying them, while subtracting one from the other divides the first by the second.

The simplest form of the slide rule has two scales, one moving and one fixed, which are marked off logarithmically. Sliding one scale along the other adds or subtracts the logarithms of the numbers shown and so multiplies or divides them.

Mechanical calculators

The first practical mechanical calculating machine was invented by French mathematician Blaise Pascal (1623–1662) in 1642 to ease the work of his father, a tax collector. The machine did simple addition and subtraction when calculations were set by moving numbered wheels.

German mathematician Gottfried Leibniz (1646–1716) made the next advance toward the end of the seventeenth century with a machine that carried out multiplication by a process of repeated addition. In turn, this led to the invention of the arithmometer in 1820 by Charles Xavier Thomas de Colmar (1785–1870) in France. This device was the first commercially successful mechanical calculator.

Further developments in the late nineteenth century produced comptometers and other machines for continuous addition and subtraction that revolutionized the jobs of financial clerks.

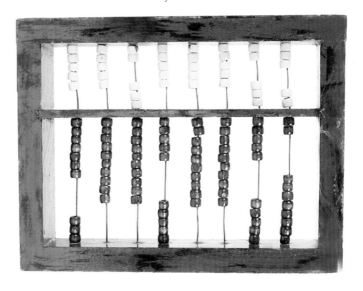

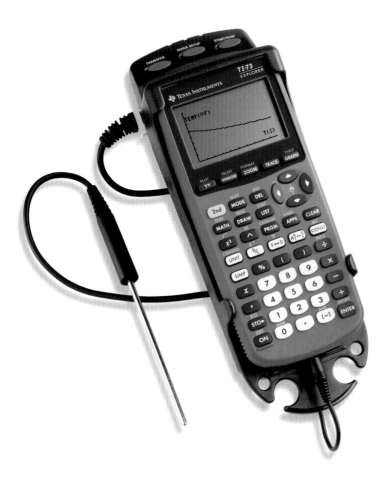

▲ *Most modern electronic calculators are capable of displaying answers as numbers or graphs. This model from Texas Instruments also has a temperature probe attached to make live temperature recordings.*

Electronic calculators

While mechanical calculators use moving parts, electronic calculators use electrical impulses and complicated integrated circuits. Early electronic calculating machines took up whole rooms and drew great amounts of power because they were made using bulky vacuum tube circuits. Today, these circuits can be formed on the surface of a tiny silicon wafer (called a silicon chip or microchip) and need very little power. As microchips became more sophisticated, calculations could be repeated with many different values or programmed as a sequence of logical steps. The more complicated calculators thus developed into microprocessors and computers of today.

Basic electronic calculators carry out the straightforward tasks of addition, subtraction, multiplication, and division. More powerful calculators have built-in facilities for storing and remembering numbers and the results of calculations. They also carry out more difficult mathematical functions automatically, such as calculating square roots or fractions, solving problems of area or volume, and evaluating normal and inverse trigonometric functions.

Memories

All electronic calculators need to hold the permanent information that controls the step-by-step workings involved in making calculations. This permanent information is stored in a read-only memory (ROM) that supplies it when necessary. A random access memory (RAM) temporarily stores the numbers produced at each stage of a calculation and feeds them back into the computation as needed.

How numbers are displayed

The user presses numbers and instructions into the calculator by touching buttons on the keyboard. The numbers entered and the results of calculations show up on the display. Early displays took a lot of electrical power to light up glowing gas discharge tubes in the shape of the numbers from 0 to 9. Modern displays use either light-emitting diodes (devices that emit light when a small current passes through them) or liquid crystals. Liquid crystals work by absorbing or reflecting light, so that they appear dark or light.

Graphing calculators

More advanced mathematical calculators can display both numbers and the graphs of mathematical functions. Many equations of interest to scientists and engineers can be thought of as looking for the values of an unknown (X) for which two functions equal each other. By plotting a graph of both functions, it is possible to locate the solutions visually.

See also: COMPUTER • MATHEMATICS • MICROELECTRONICS

Calculus

Calculus is a branch of math that describes how quantities change. Scientists rely on calculus to measure changes in many different systems. Without it, modern science and technology would not be possible.

Greek mathematician and physicist Archimedes (c. 287–212 BCE) was the first person to think about the ideas that would lead to the development of modern calculus. Archimedes was able to find the surface areas and volumes of different shapes using methods similar to the calculus that scientists and mathematicians use today.

English scientist Isaac Newton (1642–1727) and German mathematician Gottfried Wilhelm Leibniz (1646–1716) were the true founding fathers of calculus, however. In the seventeenth century, Newton and Leibniz independently discovered calculus, but their approaches were very different. Newton analyzed quantities that vary with time, whereas Leibniz looked at how small changes affect mathematical systems. Leibniz's method proved to be better, and it is his version of calculus that scientists use today.

Newton and Leibniz became involved in a bitter feud about who first discovered calculus. While it is true that Newton came up with his methods first, Leibniz was the first to publish his ideas. However, many English scientists believed that Leibniz had copied Newton's methods. This belief caused a split between English and other European scientists that lasted until early in the nineteenth century. Since Leibniz's calculus became the preferred method, English mathematicians fell out of favor. Indeed, most of the major scientific discoveries of the eighteenth century were made in mainland Europe.

What is calculus?

There are two types of calculus: differential calculus and integral calculus. Differential calculus describes how quantities change. Imagine a person walking up a hill. The steepness of the hill at any point is called the gradient, or slope, which is the height the person walks up divided by how much he or she travels across. The mathematical expression for the gradient of the hill is called the derivative. Differential calculus is the method mathematicians use to calculate derivatives.

▼ *Calculus can be used to explain the shape of a rainbow, its position in the sky, and its color.*

▶ *The gradient of a curve is its slope. The gradient in this graph is four squares up for five squares across, or four-fifths. The shaded area can be found by counting the squares—there are about twelve. Differential and integral calculus allow these values to be calculated exactly without using the graph.*

▼ *Isaac Newton (pictured below) described the principles of calculus in a paper written in 1671, but the paper remained unpublished for more than 30 years. When Leibniz published his version of calculus between 1684 and 1686, Newton branded him a cheat.*

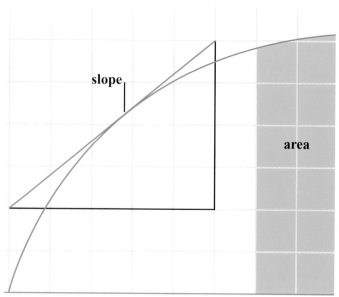

Integral calculus describes areas and volumes. Mathematicians start with an equation for the shape of an object. This equation gives the coordinates of a line or surface, similar to the way a ship's position is plotted on a map. They can then use integral calculus to convert this equation for the shape into an equation for the area or volume.

When is calculus used?

When Newton discovered calculus, he was investigating the laws of gravity and motion. He used calculus to calculate the elliptical paths, called orbits, of planets around the Sun. Scientists now use similar methods in most areas of engineering and physics. Population modeling is another important use of calculus. Populations change through birth and death, and the rate of change is modeled with differential calculus. The same methods can also predict the spread of disease and the growth of bacterial colonies.

It often happens that the rate a quantity changes depends on the amount of that quantity. For example, the rate of decay of a radioactive material, such as uranium-235, is directly proportional to the amount of material in the sample. A differential equation is a mathematical expression that relates this rate of change (the derivative) to the quantity itself. A large branch of mathematics looks at solving these complex equations.

Mathematicians have also examined calculus in more abstract ways. One such situation is to find the curvature and volume of shapes in more than three dimensions. German-born U.S. physicist Albert Einstein (1879–1955) used a generalization of calculus called differential geometry to describe gravity in his theory of general relativity. Einstein suggested that space and time should be looked at together as four-dimensional space–time. Gravity results from the curvature of space–time.

See also: ALGEBRA • ENGINEERING • MATHEMATICS • PHYSICS • POPULATION GROWTH

Camcorder

Camcorders (camera-recorders) are portable cameras that record moving pictures as video. Unlike traditional film, video is an electronic format, making it very versatile. It is easier to use and edit than film and has allowed camcorders to be made continually smaller and lighter. Because of these benefits, camcorders have become very popular with amateur users. They are used most often to record vacations and family events and to make home movies.

Camcorders first appeared on the consumer market in the 1980s and have since become an increasingly familiar sight throughout much of the world. They are particularly popular in Europe, the United States, and Japan, where most are manufactured. Camcorders can be divided into two main types—analog and digital. As camcorder technology has advanced, many different analog and digital formats have appeared. This advancing technology has meant that modern camcorders continue to offer ever-increasing picture quality, smaller dimensions, and a more sophisticated range of features than their predecessors.

Main camcorder components

All camcorders, whether analog or digital, share the same four major components: a lens, an electronic image sensor, a viewfinder, and a way in which to record images. Most also have an inbuilt microphone to record sound, and all have a selection of other operational features to help the user achieve the desired results.

▶ *A girl rides her bicycle, and her father records the action on a camcorder. Increasingly, people are using camcorders instead of ordinary cameras to record family events and holidays.*

A camcorder sees the world through a lens in the same way that a conventional camera does. Camcorders have zoom lenses that allow the user to close in on or move away from a subject without the user having to move. The lens does this by having a variable focal length. It has a wide-angle view at one extreme and a powerful telephoto (magnified) view at the other and can focus at any distance in between. Most modern camcorders have powerful zoom lenses, although this is not necessarily desirable. The more powerful the zoom, the more difficult it is to get a stable picture, as any little movement is magnified. The small size of many modern camcorders can also add to the problem, because they are not as easy to hold steady as larger models. To help counteract picture shake, many camcorders now feature image stabilization systems that determine if the camera is shaking and compensate accordingly.

The light coming through the lens of the camcorder is focused onto a small electronic semiconductor image sensor. This sensor is called a charge-coupled device (CCD). The CCD is the heart of the camcorder and is responsible for turning light into electronic signals. It is a half-inch (1.25-cm) panel of hundreds of thousands of tiny

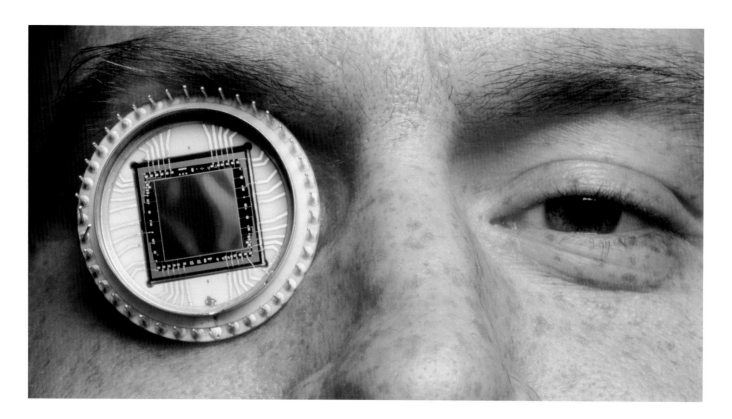

light-sensitive diodes called photosites, or pixels. These are arranged in a grid, and each pixel produces its own electrical signal when exposed to light. Generally speaking, the larger the chip, the more pixels, and so the better the quality the image.

Each pixel measures the amount of light (photons) that hits a particular point and translates this into electrons (electrical charges). A brighter image produces a higher electrical charge; a darker image a weaker charge. This difference reproduces the contrast of the image. To reproduce the color, the CCD needs to detect not only total light levels, but also the levels of each different color of light. As a full spectrum of colors can be produced by combining the three primary colors—red, green, and blue—the CCD needs only measure the levels of these colors to produce a full-color picture. It does so by using a combination of pixels that are individually sensitive to either red, green, or blue light. The computer in the camcorder then combines the information from all of the pixels to produce the full-color image.

So that the user can see what he or she is recording, the electrical video image produced by the CCD is shown in a viewfinder. Viewfinders are

▲ *A large charge-coupled device (CCD) is shown compared to the human eye. Most CCDs are much smaller than this. This one will be used in a camera on board the Hubble Space Telescope.*

actually small black-and-white or color televisions. Many camcorders also have larger full-color LCD (liquid crystal display) screens. These angle out from the camcorder and allow the user to record action without having to hold the camcorder to their eye. Although convenient, they have the disadvantage of using a lot more power than a viewfinder.

The final major component shared by all camcorders is a medium on which to record the video information. This medium is the main variable between camcorders. As camcorders record video either as analog or digital information, all of the many video formats available fall into one of these two categories.

ANALOG CAMCORDERS

The first camcorders to be developed were analog, and all camcorders worked this way until digital versions started to appear in the late 1990s. Analog technology is now becoming dated, but these camcorders are still widely used and remain popular because they are much cheaper than newer digital machines.

Analog camcorders record video and audio signals as continuously variable (analog) tracks on magnetic video tape. Their recording mechanisms are basically the same as those of a home video cassette recorder (VCR), although they may be much smaller, depending on the tape format. The various tapes (described below) are much the same as home video tape. When the camera is turned on, the electronic video signals from the CCD (and usually audio signals from a microphone) are sent to the recording heads of the cassette recorder. The magnetic polarity of the recording heads changes in relation to these signals. The tape is sensitive to these changes, and as it is wound over the heads the signals are recorded as magnetic patterns. There are several analog camcorder formats; the major ones are briefly outlined below.

Standard VHS

Standard VHS (VHS stands for Video Home System) uses the same type of videotape cassette as a regular VCR. An advantage of this is that after

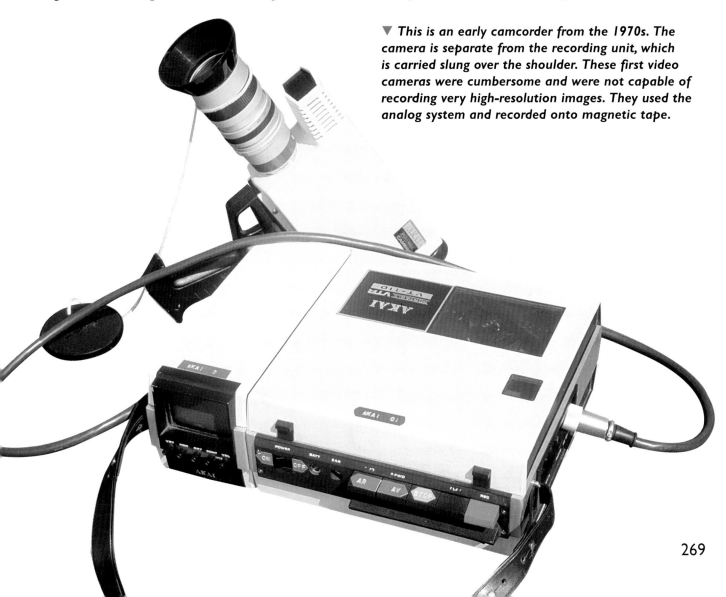

▼ *This is an early camcorder from the 1970s. The camera is separate from the recording unit, which is carried slung over the shoulder. These first video cameras were cumbersome and were not capable of recording very high-resolution images. They used the analog system and recorded onto magnetic tape.*

Super VHS

Super VHS is a higher resolution version of VHS. The cassettes are the same size, so Super VHS camcorders are still bulky. Super VHS cassettes cannot be played on a standard VCR. Instead, the camcorder has to be connected to the TV to play, or it can be connected to a VCR to be copied onto standard VHS cassettes.

Super VHS-C

Super VHS-C is a compact version of the Super VHS format. Again, this cannot be played in a VCR, but the benefit is a higher resolution and small size.

8mm

Some camcorders use small 8mm tapes about the same size as audio cassettes. Their chief advantage is compactness. Some 8mm camcorders are small enough to fit into a coat pocket. The format offers about the same resolution as standard VHS but with slightly better sound quality, and they have a similar recording time. They are more expensive than VHS cassettes, and the camcorder must be used to play the cassettes on a television.

Hi-8

Hi-8 camcorder cassettes are similar to 8mm tapes, but they have a much higher resolution (about 400 horizontal lines). They are also more expensive than ordinary 8mm tapes.

DIGITAL CAMCORDERS

Most modern camcorders are digital, and it is likely that before long all camcorders will be of this type. For the moment, however, they are still expensive compared to analog machines, and this makes them less affordable for many people.

Digital camcorders have a component that takes the analog video and audio information and translates it into digital information. Digital information is made up of 1s and 0s (known as

▲ *The Digital8 camcorder is one of the most popular camcorder formats. Digital8 camcorders are fairly small and can record high-resolution video footage. The compact size of modern camcorders means that they are easy to carry around and use.*

making a recording, the tape can simply be removed and played on most VCRs. Because of their widespread use, VHS tapes are cheap compared to other formats, and they also give a long recording time (about two hours). Their major disadvantages are size and resolution. They require a large, cumbersome camcorder design, and their resolution is low compared to more modern formats (about 230 to 250 horizontal lines).

VHS-C

VHS-C camcorders record on standard VHS tape that is contained in a more compact cassette. These can be played using an adaptor in a regular VCR, and their smaller size allows for a more compact camcorder. Their downside is that they have a shorter running time than a standard VHS cassette (about 45 minutes).

bits), and it is the information that computers use to operate. Instead of storing video and audio signals as magnetic patterns like analog machines, digital camcorders record this digital information. A major benefit of digital information is that 1s and 0s can be copied very easily without losing any of what has been recorded. Analog information, on the other hand, "fades" with each copy, as the copying process does not reproduce the original signal exactly. Also, video information in digital form can be loaded onto computers where it can be manipulated using a range of different software. As many people have home computers, this makes digital video footage easy to work with. Analog footage, on the other hand, has to be edited using the facilities on the camcorder, or on a special machine called an edit controller. The results that can be easily achieved are much more limited.

Digital information can be stored in a number of ways, and digital camcorders use many different formats. Some digital camcorders have cassette mechanisms like analog machines, but they record a digital signal onto digital tape. Others have digital video disc (DVD) drives that use lasers to record onto laser discs. Some of the latest machines have no moving recording parts at all. They store video information on microchips. The most widely used digital camcorder formats are MiniDV, Digital8, DVD, and memory cards.

MiniDV

MiniDV camcorders use compact digital cassettes. These are fairly expensive but have a high resolution (500 horizontal lines). They can hold between 60 and 90 minutes of digital video footage, which is easily transferable to a personal computer. It is also possible to store still pictures on MiniDV, in much the same way as a digital camera.

Digital8

Digital8 camcorders record digital video footage onto Hi-8 tapes. These are less expensive than MiniDV cassettes but have an almost comparable resolution. They hold less footage, however (up to 60 minutes), and Digital8 camcorders are generally larger than MiniDV ones. As with other digital camcorders, Digital8 cameras can also be connected to personal computers.

DVD

DVD camcorders do not use tape at all. Instead, they burn information onto small DVDs. These are smaller than standard DVDs, but most can be played in standard home DVD players. DVD camcorders are very similar to MiniDV ones in performance, but their picture quality is slightly better, and DVDs can store more footage (up to two hours). The main advantage of this format is that each recording session is recorded as an individual track. Instead of having to fast-forward and rewind through a cassette, it is possible to jump immediately to any desired section of video.

◀ *A girl downloads footage from a digital camcorder onto her personal computer. Because the footage is digital, the computer can understand it. Using special software, the footage can be cut and edited. The finished movie can then be recorded onto a DVD.*

Memory cards

Memory cards are the latest format to be developed for camcorders. SD cards, Memory Sticks, and Flash memory cards are the most widely used. These are solid-state memory chips, which are both very small and also do not require mechanical recording heads like cassettes and disks. This means that the camcorders can be smaller and lighter than ever. Also, as with DVD, different recording sessions can be accessed immediately.

VIDEO EDITING

Camcorders have various control functions that help the user to achieve certain results while they are recording. However carefully it is shot, though, raw, unedited footage is disjointed, contains a lot of

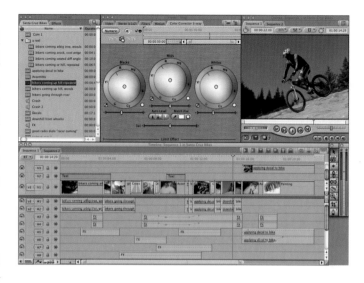

▲ **This is the main window view of the video editing program Final Cut Pro. Digital video footage can be cut and edited on a home computer using such specialized software, enabling the user to create professional looking results.**

> ### DID YOU KNOW?
>
> Camcorders use special rechargeable batteries. Advances in battery technology have been as important to the evolution of camcorders as any of the more noticeable technological changes. Modern camcorders place high demands on batteries, and the latest Lithium-ion (Li-ion) batteries produce more power for longer periods, recharge more times, and are smaller than ever. The next generation of polymer batteries are expected to be even better.

"junk" shots, and looks amateurish. To achieve a more professional look, it needs to be edited. To do this, all camcorders come with sockets for getting the footage out of the camcorder and into a VCR, edit controller, or computer.

Basic editing can be done using the camcorder and a VCR. Analog video is often edited in this way. Clips of video and soundtrack from the original recording are selectively copied in the desired order from the camcorder onto a VHS cassette. This produces a basic "cut" version. For easier editing and more advanced effects, however, footage has to be copied to an edit controller or a computer.

Modern, digital footage is usually edited on computer. Digital footage is downloaded, or "captured" to computer using fast FireWire connections, as video data files can be very large. The video files are then opened using video-editing software. Popular examples include Apple's Final Cut Pro, Adobe Premiere, and Pinnacle Systems' Studio DV. Video-editing software makes editing straightforward, although it can get more complicated with advanced effects. A simple edit might involve first selecting the best or most appropriate clips and, if necessary, adjusting their color or contrast levels (or perhaps using effects such as sepia, black and white, or wide-screen). The clips would then be linked together, maybe using transition effects such as "dissolves," "wipes," or "fades." Other effects, such as titles or credits, could also be added. Finally the soundtrack, or separate music or commentary, would be overlaid. With some practice, an amateur's results can be very hard to tell apart from a professional production.

> *See also:* COMPUTER • LASER DISC • LIGHT •
> MAGNETIC STORAGE • MOTION PICTURE •
> PHOTOGRAPHY • PHOTOGRAPHY, DIGITAL

Canal

Canals are artificial waterways built mainly as shipping routes. They reduce the distances ships have to travel. For example, a cargo ship traveling from New York to San Francisco can use the Panama Canal and save 7,800 miles (12,600 kilometers) on the journey. Canals are also built for irrigation, water supply, and drainage.

Across the world, vast networks of canals shortcut entire continents and carry traffic into the heart of industrial areas. Heavy loads can be moved relatively cheaply and, at the same time, they are kept off the busy highways.

Canals are like artificial rivers, but they are built to run as far as possible on one level. Keeping the same level may mean constructing aqueducts to carry the canal across valleys, or tunnels to take it through hills. Sometimes the level of a canal does have to change—for example, where a canal meets a river or the sea—to allow ships to complete their journey. Changing the level may mean lifting boats up and down a slope, using a ship lift that raises and lowers a basin of water in which the boat floats. Alternatively, the level of a canal can be changed by constructing a series of locks.

The first canals

Canals were first used to supply water to people and crops. They were vital to all the ancient civilizations of the Middle East and the Mediterranean region. In the Middle East, only one canal was built to carry boats. Construction started in Suez around 600 BCE to link the Red Sea with the east bank of the Nile Delta. This early canal was wide enough to allow two ships to pass at the same time.

Unlike the Middle East, China built most of its canals for navigation. China's three large rivers flow mostly from west to east. Food was grown mostly in the south and had to be transported to the north.

▼ *The Suez Canal has been open for navigation since November 17, 1869. It is a very important trade route, linking the Mediterranean Sea with the Red Sea. If the Suez Canal did not exist, ships would have to navigate the Cape of Good Hope to make the same journey.*

▲ *Laborers work on Boulters Lock on the Thames River near Maidenhead, England, in 1912. Canals were also called navigations, and the men who built them were known as navigators, or "navvies."*

Construction of the waterway that was to become the Grand Canal began in the fourth century BCE. It connected the Chang Jiang River to the the city of Huaiyin in Jiangsu sheng (province). Around 250 years after work started, the Great Canal had been built as far as Hangzhou in Zhejiang sheng (province), 220 miles (355 kilometers) south of the Chang Jiang River. This huge construction was not finished until 1330 CE, when it reached Beijing. It is now more than 1,000 miles (1,600 kilometers) long.

Chinese engineers develop the lock

When the Chinese engineers first started to design this waterway, they realized that the land rose about 50 feet (15 meters) between the Chang Jiang River and the Huai He River. Some way had to be found to get the boats up this rise. So the Chinese engineers came up with the lock as a solution.

Locks probably developed from dams built across rivers to hold back floodwater. Boats had to navigate through a gateway in these dams. People realized that building two dams close together, to enclose a short stretch of water, would provide a chamber with a level that could be changed to match the level above or below the double gates.

The first lock was built with a ramp as the canal bed. It consisted of a solid wood gate at the lower end only. Two stone pillars with grooves on the inside were placed on each side of the ramp. Logs with ropes attached to their ends were fitted into the grooves. The logs were raised with the ropes to release the stored water.

Other locks had guillotine gates, which slid straight up and down. Later, locks were built of masonry with double gates swinging across each end, angled in such a way that the pressure of water from the higher side would force them shut tight.

HOW A POUND LOCK WORKS

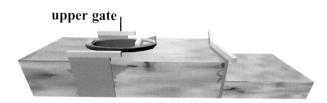

upper gate

When a boat needs to move downstream, the upper gates are opened. The lower gates remain closed. The skipper then moves the boat inside the lock.

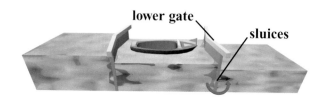

lower gate · sluices

When the boat is inside the lock, the upper gates are closed. The sluices in the lower gates open to release water from the lock and lower the boat.

When the water inside the lock reaches the lower level, the lower gates are opened. The skipper then moves the boat slowly out of the lock.

When the lower gates are closed again, the sluices in the upper gate open up, raising the water level in the lock. It is now ready for the next boat to pass through.

However, water is lost every time a boat descends from one stretch of the canal to another through a lock, so reservoirs and feeder channels have to be built near the canal system to keep the water level constantly at its highest point.

By the eleventh century, the Dutch found a way of building locks without knowing about the Chinese system. The Dutch design, called a pound lock, is still used today. It has a gate at the top and bottom, and sluices (small gates) in the main gates to allow the water to fill and empty gradually (see the illustration on the opposite page).

Canal routes

Many early canals were called contour canals. They followed the natural contours of the land to avoid the cost of major construction works, so the route tended to be indirect. Once the engineers decided to build aqueducts and tunnels, they planned canals that ran directly from point to point.

The first canal to run directly up and over high ground was the Canal de Briare, which links the Loire River to the Seine River in France. The Canal de Briare is 21 miles (34 kilometers) long, and it has 40 locks to raise it over a 266-feet (81-meter) summit level. From the day it opened in 1642 it proved a commercial success, taking payment (tolls) from the boats that used it.

Boat lifts

Going through locks takes up a lot of time. Boats have to wait for each lock to fill or empty before moving on to the next. Locks also use up a lot of water to maintain the highest level of the canal. An alternative to locks are boat lifts, which raise or lower the boat in one swoop.

Boat lifts are not a modern invention. Originally, boats were winched up by means of a capstan (a drum with cable wound around it) at the higher

▶ *The Isthmus of Corinth is cut by the Corinth Canal. A French company, the Société Internationale du Canal Maritime de Corinth, started excavating the canal in 1882, but work stopped seven years later when the company went bankrupt. The Corinth Canal was completed by the Greeks in 1893.*

end. When a boat had to go down the canal, the skipper had to steer it through the tumbling water with no assistance.

Boat lifts are still in use today. One example links a canal to the Elbe River in Germany. The lift picks up a boat in a "tub" of water and carries it up 126 feet (38 meters), which is the difference in levels between canal and river. Steel gates hold the water in the tub and close off the ends of the canal and river entrances. Four huge concrete towers house the lifting equipment. The tub is fitted with electric motors and gears that let it climb up ladders built into the towers.

Canals today

Canals enjoyed a brief heyday during the Industrial Revolution of the eighteenth and nineteenth centuries. When the railroads came, many canals

▶ *An electric locomotive, known as a "mule," helps guide a container ship through the Miraflores Locks on the Panama Canal. Miraflores Locks is the first set of locks at the Pacific entrance to the canal.*

were allowed to fall into disrepair. In mainland Europe, canals and railroads continued to develop side by side. Certain trunk canal routes have been improved and enlarged over the years because people realized that they provided an attractive way of carrying bulk cargoes over long distances.

Today in Europe there are major canal networks in Belgium, France, Germany, and the Netherlands. These canals also cross over the countries' borders, improving shipping and trade routes. In North America, the New York State Barge Canal can take 2,500-ton (2,270-tonne) craft, while the St. Lawrence Seaway—part canal, part river— enables huge seagoing vessels to travel from Montreal to Lake Ontario and on into Lake Erie.

The Panama and Suez Canals

Perhaps the most impressive canals are the Suez Canal, which links the Mediterranean Sea and the Red Sea, and the Panama Canal, which links the Atlantic and Pacific Oceans. The Suez Canal eliminates the need to travel around the Cape of Good Hope in South Africa. The Panama Canal cuts out Cape Horn in South America.

The Suez Canal was built in the late nineteenth century. Engineers did not have to build locks for this canal because it was at sea level. Ships can pass straight through without having to negotiate lock gates. The Panama Canal, which was completed in 1914, rises 85 feet (26 meters) above sea level. It does have a system of locks. An artificial lake at the top level of the canal gathers water that supplies the locks. Unfortunately, both the Suez Canal and Panama Canal cannot cope with the increasing size of modern ships. It is no longer possible for the largest ships—the supertankers—to pass through either the Suez Canal or Panama Canal.

Inland waterways of the United States

Another major system is the network of 6,000 miles (10,000 kilometers) of inland waterways formed by the Mississippi River, its tributaries, and their associated canals in the United States. The inland waterways that form this vast network are normally just 9 feet (3 meters) deep. The smallest locks measure 600 by 100 feet (180 by 30 meters).

In the southern states, the Mississippi system links up with the Intracoastal Waterway. This combination of natural channels and lock-free canals allows barges and other small craft to move along the coast while sheltered from the sea.

See also: ENGINEERING • SHIP AND SHIPBUILDING

Capacitor

Available in all shapes and sizes, capacitors are used in almost every type of electronic equipment, such as radios and televisions. Their job is to store and to help regulate the flow of electricity (electrical current) that passes through a machine's circuits.

A capacitor, also called a condenser, is one of the simplest electronic devices. It is used to store electrical charge and control the flow of electricity within a device. All capacitors have a similar design, consisting of two metal plates set a small distance apart. Between the plates is insulating material (a material that does not conduct electricity), which may be a solid, liquid, or gas.

When an electric current is passed into a capacitor, the metal plates store electrical charge; positive charge on one plate and negative charge on the other plate. These charges then become the supplies of electricity and can be released or shut off as required. The ability of a capacitor to store an electric charge is referred to as its capacitance.

Capacitors in action

Suppose that the two plates of a capacitor are connected to the terminals of a battery. If a 9V battery is used, then there will be a voltage (electrical pressure) of 9 volts across the capacitor, too. In other words, the capacitor is storing electrical charges from the battery. The battery acts as an electricity pump. It tries to force the electrical charges, in the form of tiny particles called electrons, around an electrical circuit.

When the capacitor is connected to the battery, electrons start to flow from the negative pole of the battery, along the connecting wire, and into one plate of the capacitor. Electrons are negative charges, so the plate becomes negatively charged.

Meanwhile, the other plate of the capacitor loses its electrons to the positive pole of the battery along the other connecting wire. Positively charged protons stay in place, so as the electrons leave, the plate acquires an overall positive charge.

The charging current

There is not one continuous flow of electrons passing around the circuit, but, in effect, two separate flows. One flows from the negative terminal of the battery to one side of the capacitor. The other flows from the other side of the capacitor to the positive battery terminal. No current actually passes through the capacitor because the insulating substance between the plates (called the dielectric) does not conduct electricity. This flow of electrons is called an electric current.

The electric current

In some ways, the flow of electricity and water are similar—they are both called currents. Suppose a small hole is made in the bottom of a tin can. If the can is pushed a little way into some water, the can will start to fill. Pressure forces the water in through

▶ *Capacitors vary in size and type, depending on the applications in which they are to be used, but the way in which they work is the same.*

▶ *This electric circuit board contains a number of capacitors, for example, the yellow cylinders. Capacitors can regulate the flow of current in a circuit.*

the hole. The water will continue to flow until the level inside the container is the same as the level outside. The pressure on each side of the hole will then be the same, and the water will stop flowing.

In the case of electricity, a current may flow between points where the voltage (electrical pressure) is different. If two points are at the same voltage, then no current will flow between them.

When the battery is first connected to the uncharged capacitor, a heavy current flows because the voltage across the capacitor is zero, while that across the battery is 9 volts. The heavy current flow is caused by the difference in electrical pressure. As the plates of the capacitor become charged, the voltage across them increases, so the voltage

▼ *This illustration shows the electron flow across a capacitor. When the switch is closed, the battery pumps electrons from one capacitor plate to the other until the potential difference (voltage) between the plates equals the voltage of the battery.*

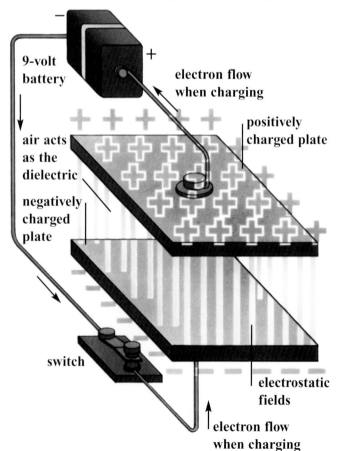

difference between the battery and capacitor decreases. As a result, the current flowing around the circuit falls. Eventually, the voltage across the capacitor reaches 9 volts. When the capacitor and battery are both at the same voltage, no more current flows. The electrical pressure at each end of the conductor is the same.

Switching off the capacitor

If the battery is disconnected, the capacitor will stay charged. It could even remain charged forever if it had a perfect insulator between the plates. But no insulator is perfect, so a small current always leaks across the dielectric. Eventually, the original balance of positive and negative charges on the two plates is restored. This process is called discharging.

The capacitor can also be discharged much more quickly through a wire or some other component, such as a flash bulb. After a battery has charged up a flash's capacitor over several seconds, the capacitor then dumps the full charge into the flash bulb almost instantly. This happens so quickly that a capacitor may be charged and discharged millions of times every second. In this way, capacitors can even out a voltage supply by absorbing the peaks and filling in the valleys.

See also: ELECTRIC CIRCUIT • ELECTRICITY

Carbohydrate

Carbohydrates are one of the three major types of food needed by all living things. The other two are fats and proteins. Carbohydrates are a source of energy that is released when breathing. Marathon runners eat pasta (high in carbohydrates) before a race.

▲ Carbohydrates are found in many different foods. Foods particularly rich in carbohydrates include wheat products, such as bread and pasta. These foods contain starch, a polysaccharide carbohydrate.

Carbohydrates are made up of just three chemical elements—carbon, oxygen, and hydrogen. As in water (H_2O), there are two parts of hydrogen (H) to each part of oxygen (O). So carbohydrates can be thought of as combinations of carbon and water. This explains how carbohydrates got their name. The general term for a substance containing water is a hydrate. So any combination of carbon and water became known as a hydrate of carbon, or a carbohydrate.

Carbohydrates are divided into four major groups. As many carbohydrates are sweet, the names of these groups come from the Greek word for sugar, *sakkharon*. The four groups are monosaccharides, disaccharides, oligosaccharides, and polysaccharides.

MONOSACCHARIDES

Monosaccharides are the simplest form of carbohydrates and are often called simple sugars. They are made from just one molecule, containing from three to nine carbon atoms. These are usually arranged in a chain.

Most monosaccharides consist of molecules with five or six carbon atoms. A monosaccharide that contains five carbon atoms is called a pentose. A monosaccharide with six carbon atoms is called a hexose. The most important monosaccharides are glucose (also called dextrose or grape sugar) and fructose (fruit sugar).

Glucose and fructose

Glucose is the most common hexose form of monosaccharide. It occurs naturally in fruits and honey. Glucose is an important energy source in plants and animals. Plants make glucose by combining water with carbon dioxide from the air in a process called photosynthesis. This process takes place in sunlight. Some of the energy from the Sun's rays is converted into chemical energy stored in the glucose. In plants, stored glucose molecules are linked to form long chain molecules of starch.

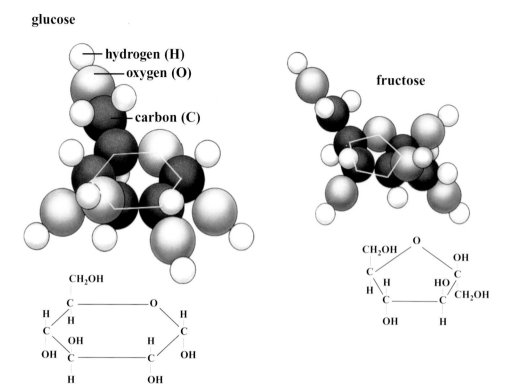

glucose

— hydrogen (H)
— oxygen (O)
— carbon (C)

fructose

This illustration shows the arrangement of atoms in the two common simple sugar molecules, glucose and fructose. These sugars are the basic building blocks of most of the larger carbohydrates.

This photograph of German chemist Emil Fischer was taken some time after 1904. Fischer was famed for his studies of sugars. In 1887, he was the first person to make glucose in the laboratory. Glucose synthesis is a difficult process, so now the sugar is produced commercially by breaking down larger carbohydrates, such as starch.

Animals are unable to make their own glucose. They get their supply by eating plants or other animals. Some glucose always circulates in the blood. Stored glucose molecules in animals are linked together to form long chain molecules of a substance called glycogen. Glycogen is stored in muscle cells and the liver. Both glycogen in animals and starch in plants are examples of chain molecules called polymers.

Fructose is the second most common simple sugar, or monosaccharide. Fructose, along with glucose, occurs in fruits and honey. It also occurs in certain vegetables. Fructose has to be converted into glucose before it can be used by the body. It is often converted to fat, rather than glycogen.

Manufacturing glucose

Glucose was first manufactured in the laboratory in 1887 by German chemist Emil Fischer (1852–1919). However, it is difficult to imitate the natural processes that occur in plants because the carbon, hydrogen, and oxygen can combine in so many different ways. Glucose is just one of 16

possible monosaccharides, all with the chemical formula $C_6H_{16}O_6$. Only three of these different structures, called isomers, occur in nature.

Plants contain substances called enzymes that control the way in which the carbon, hydrogen, and oxygen combine. As a result, a plant can produce just one of the isomers (glucose, for example). In a laboratory process, with no enzymes present, a mixture of isomers is produced.

Most glucose produced commercially is obtained from starch. Starch consists of glucose molecules linked together. When glucose molecules link up, water is released. So, to break down a starch chain into glucose, the water molecules must be replaced. This process is called hydrolysis. The glucose is used for making jams, syrups, and candies.

DISACCHARIDES

A carbohydrate called a disaccharide is formed when two monosaccharides join together. For example, when glucose and fructose join in a

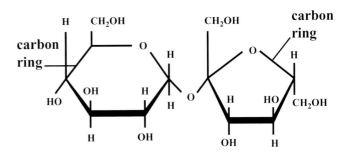

▼ *The disaccharide sucrose (sugar) consists of glucose (left) and fructose (right) linked by oxygen.*

certain way, the disaccharide called sucrose is formed. Sucrose is commonly known as sugar. It is an important ingredient in many foods.

On average, a person in a developed country consumes more than 100 pounds (45 kilograms) of sucrose each year. It is obtained from sugar cane, sugar beet, and sugar maple. These crops contain up to 20 percent by weight of sucrose.

A disaccharide called maltose consists of two glucose molecules linked together. Maltose is formed when grain starts to grow, because pairs of glucose molecules start to break away from the long starch chains in the grain. Other disaccharides include lactose and galactose, both found in milk.

OLIGOSACCHARIDES AND POLYSACCHARIDES

When three to six monosaccharides join up, the carbohydrate is called an oligosaccharide. If there are more than six monosaccharides joined together, the carbohydrate is known as a polysaccharide. Oligosaccharides are not often found in nature, but polysaccharides are very common. These are powdery substances, usually insoluble in water and tasteless. The numerous types of polysaccharides include starch and cellulose.

Starch

Starch is stored in the seeds and tubers (swollen roots) of plants. It is used by the developing plants as a food supply. Many glucose molecules link together to form spiral chains of starch. This structure makes the starch tend to form into grains.

DID YOU KNOW?

Fruits and vegetables are rich sources of certain types of carbohydrates.

Strawberries and many other fruits contain the simple sugars, or monosaccharides, glucose and fructose.

Potatoes are the tubers of the potato plant. They are energy stores for the plant, containing the polysaccharide carbohydrate starch.

281

▲ *Plant cells are made from the polysaccharide carbohydrate cellulose. Cellulose is made from many glucose molecules linked together to form long, straight chains. Cellulose is tough and fibrous and helps make the cells rigid.*

Starch occurs in two forms called amylopectin and amylose. It is used in foods, adhesives, and medicines. It is also used as a specialized type of finishing for paper and textiles.

Cellulose

Like starch, cellulose is made up of many glucose molecules linked together. But, in cellulose, the glucose molecules form straight chains. This gives cellulose its fibrous nature. It forms the main part of natural fibers, such as cotton, wood, flax, and hemp. It occurs in the cell walls of plants.

Cellulose is used in the manufacture of many important products. These include the explosives nitroglycerin and guncotton, imitation leather, and artificial fibers. Two main types of the artificial fiber rayon are made using cellulose.

DID YOU KNOW?

Sugar structures

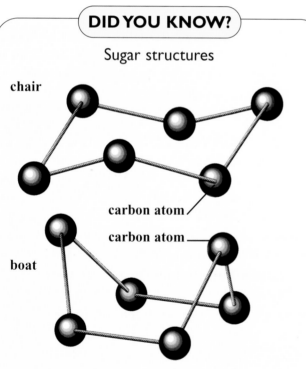

chair

carbon atom

carbon atom

boat

Sugar molecules can curl up on themselves and form ring-shaped molecules when two parts of the same molecule react together. This happens when sugars solidify (become solid). The rings tend to form one of two shapes—a chair shape or a boat shape.

See also: ATOM AND MOLECULE • CARBON • NUTRITION • WATER

282

Carbon

Carbon is a substance that is necessary to life. Plants get their carbon from the air, and animals obtain it from plants or other animals. Carbon is found in several forms, including diamond, the hardest natural substance, and graphite, which is soft and slippery.

Carbon is found in more than one million chemical compounds. The study of carbon and its compounds is called organic chemistry because carbon is essential to life and is found in all kinds of organisms. Carbon is also found within Earth, in water, and in the atmosphere.

Most life-forms, from the simple, single-celled amoeba to humans, contain a wide range of carbon compounds. Animals get their carbon by eating plants, or other animals that eat plants. Green plants get their carbon from carbon dioxide in the air, through photosynthesis. Photosynthesis is the process in which green plants and certain other organisms use light energy to convert water, carbon dioxide, and minerals into oxygen and energy-rich organic compounds.

Carbon dioxide in the air is being replaced all the time. It is given off by animals when they breathe out. Without animals, there would not be enough carbon dioxide for plants. Without plants, animals would not be able to obtain the carbon they need.

Carbon chemistry, therefore, provides important links between plant and animal life. The series of reactions that takes place is called the carbon cycle.

▼ *Food is often cooked over a charcoal fire. As the charcoal burns it releases impurities, which give the food its barbecue flavor. Eating too much barbecued food may be harmful.*

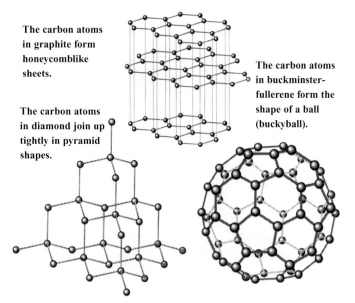

The carbon atoms in graphite form honeycomblike sheets.

The carbon atoms in buckminster-fullerene form the shape of a ball (buckyball).

The carbon atoms in diamond join up tightly in pyramid shapes.

naturally as three main allotropes—diamond, graphite, and fullerene. Many other forms of carbon occur in nature or can be made artificially, but they are all modified forms of graphite. These include charcoal, coke, and various forms of soot. Unlike the main allotropes, they show little sign of a crystalline structure, so they are classified as amorphous (shapeless) allotropes of carbon.

Diamond

Diamond is a clear, crystalline form of carbon. It is the hardest substance found in nature and is widely used in drilling, cutting, and grinding tools. Diamond is expensive because it is rare. It is mined

▲ *The way in which carbon atoms are joined in carbon allotropes determines the properties of the substance. The rigid structure of bonds in diamond creates a very hard substance. The flat bonds in graphite make a weak substance. Buckyballs have a strong structure.*

Where carbon is found

Although carbon is essential to life, it is surprising how little pure carbon is found naturally on Earth. Only a very small fraction of Earth's crust is composed of pure carbon. Most carbon is found combined with other substances to form compounds. Some minerals are carbon-containing compounds known as carbonates. Limestone and chalk, for example, are made of calcium carbonate ($CaCO_3$). Marble is a combination of calcium carbonate and magnesium carbonate. Sediments from dead plants form deposits with a high carbon content. These include peat, coal, oil, and gas. They provide important sources of energy.

Carbon allotropes

Carbon occurs in several forms called allotropes. Allotropes are different physical forms of the same element. All the allotropes of an element give rise to identical chemical compounds. Carbon occurs

▶ *The pear-shaped Millennium Star is one of the largest diamonds in the world. Perfectly clear, or flawless, diamonds are highly prized, and the Millennium Star is virtually priceless.*

DID YOU KNOW?

Carbon is an unusual element. Carbon atoms can join up in long chains. These chains can then join at each end to make carbon rings.

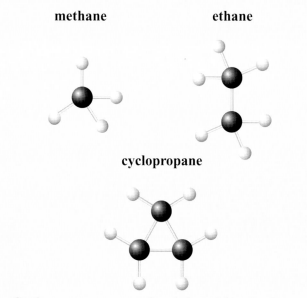

methane **ethane**

cyclopropane

Carbon atoms can also join with more than one bond. Some carbon compounds have double bonds, such as ethene, or sometimes triple bonds, such as ethyne. These compounds are less stable than those with single bonds.

is a good conductor of electricity and is used to make the carbon brushes (contacts) in some electric motors. Another important use is in nuclear reactors. Here graphite is used as a moderator—a substance that reduces the speed of fast-moving neutrons—to control the nuclear fission process, which releases energy. The most common use of graphite is as pencil "lead." It is called lead simply because graphite resembles lead in appearance. The name graphite, however, resulted from the use of graphite in pencils and comes from the Greek word meaning "to write."

Fullerenes

Fullerenes are the third form of pure carbon. U.S. scientists Richard E. Smalley (1943–) and Robert F. Curl Jr. (1933–) and English scientist Harold W. Kroto (1939–) discovered the first fullerene in 1985. By using lasers to vaporize graphite rods in an atmosphere of helium gas, they produced a compound composed of 60 carbon atoms (C_{60}). The atoms are joined together by single or double bonds to form a hollow sphere with 12 pentagonal (five-sided) spheres and 20 hexagonal (six-sided) faces—a design resembling a soccer ball. Fullerenes get their name from the U.S. architect R. Buckminster Fuller (1895–1983), whose dome designs are similar to the molecular structure of C_{60}. Buckminsterfullerene, or buckyball, is the name given to a C_{60} allotrope.

Amorphous carbon

Wood charcoal is made by heating wood to a high temperature in the absence of oxygen. Gases are driven off from the wood, and charcoal is left. Powdered charcoal is used to make gunpowder. Activated charcoal is a very absorbent form of wood charcoal. It is made by heating sawdust in a little air and steam. Activated charcoal is used in air-conditioning units to absorb odors. It is also used in gas masks to absorb poisonous gases. Charcoal burns at a high temperature. Meat can be given a pleasant flavor by cooking it over a charcoal fire. The flavor comes from the compounds produced when fat drips onto the hot charcoals and vaporizes.

mainly in South Africa and Brazil. The larger crystals with few impurities and imperfections are used as gemstones. They are carefully cut to shape so that they reflect as much light as possible. This gives the final stones their sparkle. Small traces of impurities in the diamonds give them a slight color.

In nature, diamond is formed when another kind of carbon is compressed at a high temperature. But it was not until the 1950s that scientists found out how to do this artificially. Today, artificial diamonds are widely used in industry to make cutting tools and abrasives.

Graphite

Graphite is a soft, gray-black crystalline form of carbon. Its slippery quality makes it suitable for lubricating the moving parts of machines. Graphite

Animal charcoal, sometimes called boneblack, is made from bones. When bones are heated in the absence of oxygen, a thin layer of charcoal forms on the surface of the bones. One of the main uses of animal charcoal is to absorb impurities from oils and sugars.

Lampblack is a kind of soot. It is formed when oil is burned with little oxygen. The black powder is used to color inks and paints. It is also used as the coating on carbon paper.

Carbon black is the soot formed when natural gas is burned with little oxygen. It is a finer powder than lampblack, and so is more commonly used in inks and paints. Carbon black is also added to the rubber in automobile tires. It acts as a filler, which helps make tires last longer.

Carbon monoxide and carbon dioxide

The poisonous gas carbon monoxide (CO) is formed when carbon burns in a limited supply of oxygen. Some carbon monoxide is formed in automobile engines because not all the fuel is

▲ *Vehicle engines produce small amounts of poisonous carbon monoxide gas when they burn gasoline. When high levels of this gas build up (in congested cities, for example) it causes serious pollution.*

burned. In heavy traffic, carbon monoxide can build up to a dangerous level. The gas is used in industry to obtain metals from their ores. In a blast furnace, for example, carbon monoxide removes oxygen from iron ore, reducing it to iron. In this process, the carbon monoxide is converted, or oxidized, to carbon dioxide (CO_2).

Carbon dioxide is formed when carbon burns in an abundant supply of oxygen. The gas, which is heavier than air, is not poisonous, but it can cause suffocation. One of its main uses is to add the fizziness to carbonated drinks. Carbon dioxide freezes at $-56.6°C$ ($-70°F$) to form a solid substance called dry ice. This is often used for stage effects.

See also: BLAST FURNACE • CARBON FIBER • DIAMOND • FOOD WEB

Carbon dating

Carbon dating is a method that allows archaeologists to calculate the ages of specimens between 5,000 and 50,000 years old. It relies on radioactivity from carbon found in the remains of animals and plant matter.

In 1947, U.S. chemist Willard Libby (1908–1980) made a discovery that would provide a simple way to measure the ages of many types of archaeological specimens. He discovered that the carbon found in animal and vegetable remains is weakly radioactive, and that older samples are less radioactive than newer ones. (Radiation is a stream of particles or electromagnetic waves emitted by the decaying nuclei of atoms. This decay can take from fractions of a second to more than one billion years.) Using radiation from samples whose ages he knew, Libby showed that the strength of radiation detected in a sample can tell its age. This work earned Libby the 1960 Nobel Prize for chemistry.

Radioactive carbon

Carbon atoms exist in three different forms, called isotopes. Each isotope has six protons but a different number of neutrons in each nucleus. The most common carbon isotope is carbon-12. It has six neutrons in each nucleus. Around one carbon atom in every hundred has an extra neutron that makes it carbon-13. The other carbon isotope, carbon-14, has eight neutrons and is the rarest of all. Only one in a trillion (1,000,000,000,000) carbon atoms in the atmosphere is carbon-14.

Carbon-14 is unstable. Every so often, a carbon-14 atom releases an electron as it becomes a nitrogen-14 atom. This process is an example of radioactive decay, and each decay releases radiation that scientists can measure with a device called a Geiger counter. The decays happen as randomly as popping corn in a hot pan, but it is still possible to predict the proportion of carbon-14 atoms that decay in a given amount of time. Precise measurements show that it takes 5,730 years for half the carbon-14 in a sample to decay. This time is the "half-life" of the carbon-14 isotope.

◄ *This photograph of Willard Libby was taken on September 15, 1954, the day that Dwight D. Eisenhower, 34th president of the United States, announced Libby's appointment to the Atomic Energy Commission. Libby discovered the method of carbon dating seven years earlier when he was professor of chemistry at the Institute for Nuclear Studies at the University of Chicago.*

Where is carbon-14 from?

The half-life of carbon-14 is short compared to the age of Earth, so it might seem strange that carbon-14 still appears on Earth. In fact, a process high in the atmosphere constantly replaces the carbon-14 that decays. Cosmic rays (fast-moving particles from outer space) drive the process. First, a cosmic ray smashes an atom to release fast-moving particles. Then, a fast-moving neutron from that atom hits a nitrogen-14 atom and converts it into carbon-14.

Carbon-14 gets into plants as carbon dioxide that the plants use to form starches and sugars as they grow. Humans and other animals take in carbon-14 when they feed on plants or animals, so all living matter contains the same proportion of carbon-14 as the atmosphere that surrounds it.

Dating

The ratio of carbon-14 to carbon-12 starts to drop as soon as a plant or animal dies, because it stops taking in carbon-14. When Willard Libby started work on carbon dating, he guessed that the amount of carbon-14 in the atmosphere had always been the same. He then calculated ages from the amounts of carbon-14 remaining in samples. His carbon-dating results were a reasonable match for the historical ages of samples from 5,000-year-old

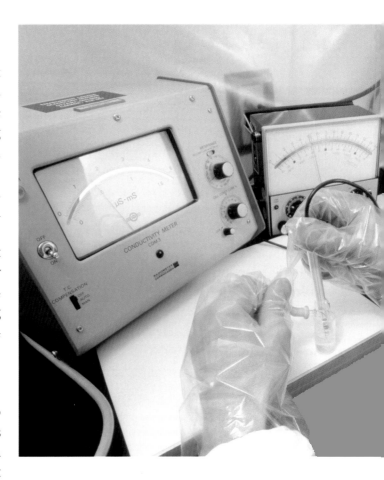

▲ *A scientist measures carbon dioxide levels in a glacial ice core sample. By determining the amount of carbon-14 in the sample, it is possible to calculate its age with reasonable accuracy.*

Egyptian tombs and other sites. Wooden items, textiles, and bones are all suitable for dating. The most accurate carbon-dating results use carbon-14 levels from old living trees, such as bristlecone pines. These trees can live for more than five thousand years. Samples from their yearly rings allow scientists to calculate the small variations in atmospheric carbon-14 through their lives. Older records of carbon-14 levels come from matching the rings in trees whose lives overlapped. Scientists have been able to calculate the ages of rings in tree remains up to ten thousand years old. Knowing the age of a tree ring, archaeologists can determine levels of carbon-14 from that time.

DID YOU KNOW?

Future archaeologists will have a complex task dating objects from the twentieth century onward. The proportion of carbon-14 in the atmosphere dipped by around two to three percent in the first half of the century as carbon dioxide from burning ancient reserves of coal and oil increased the proportion of carbon-12 in the atmosphere. The 1950s saw a more drastic change as nuclear test explosions increased the proportion of carbon-14 in the atmosphere by more than half its original value.

See also: ARCHAEOLOGY • CARBON • GEIGER COUNTER • RADIOACTIVITY

Carbon fiber

Carbon fibers are strands of material heated to give them amazing strength. They can also resist high temperatures and strong chemicals. Carbon fibers are usually used together with certain other materials and have a wide variety of high-tech uses.

During the last century, various uses have been found for carbon fibers. A well-known example was Thomas Edison's use of carbon fibers for the filaments in his early electric lamps. These fibers were made by heating linen and cotton. Edison's carbon filaments were able to withstand high temperatures for some time before they eventually burned out.

Carbon fibers also resist physical or chemical change, even at high temperatures. This makes them extremely useful in many industrial processes. They can be used to make materials for filtering hot, corrosive liquids and gases. They can also be used for insulating objects at very high temperatures. However, carbon fibers made from linen and cotton can break easily. It was not until the 1950s that strong carbon fibers suitable for reinforcement were made. This innovation created many more uses for the material.

Making carbon fibers

The first strong carbon fibers were made to reinforce a type of plastic called phenolic resin. The fibers were made from strands of viscose rayon, which is a form of synthetic fiber. Rapid progress in carbon-fiber technology followed in the 1960s, and scientists produced stronger and more effective materials.

▼ *The wings of this powered glider are made of carbon fiber. They are light and flexible, yet strong, and can also withstand the changes in temperature and weather conditions that the glider will experience.*

Carbon fibers are made by a process called pyrolysis, which means decomposition by heat. The material that starts the process is called the precursor, or starter, and it must be a fiber that contains carbon. It must also keep its fibrous form throughout the heat treatment and must leave a final residue that contains a lot of carbon.

Various natural and synthetic materials that contain carbon may be used to start the process. Natural cellulose fibers, such as cotton, hemp, and flax, do not give much carbon, so the quality of their carbon fibers is poor. One of the first synthetic starters to make a major improvement in the quality of the carbon fibers was viscose rayon. But the greatest advances have been made with a material called polyacrylonitrile (PAN). These fibers are similar to those used in commercial

> ## DID YOU KNOW?
>
> Depending on what the carbon fiber is to be used for, after it has been heat processed it can be milled (ground), chopped, or woven into different types of cloth before being mixed with a matrix.

acrylic fabrics. Other important starting fibers including polyvinyl alcohol, polyimide, and polyamides. Various pitch fibers (made from tar) and specially treated woolen fibers are also practical starting materials.

Commercial production

A lengthy heat treatment is needed to convert a starter material into carbon fiber. The atmosphere, temperature, time, and tension of the fibers must all be carefully controlled. Otherwise it is impossible to produce carbon fibers that are all of the same quality.

▼ *A technician checks machinery used in the manufacture of carbon fiber. Black carbon fiber threads are wound onto spools on the machine. These threads will then be woven into cloth. Carbon fiber cloth can be used to make a variety of products.*

The fibers are sometimes heated by putting small batches of about 10,000 strands into separate furnaces. Another method is to pass the fibers through several furnaces in a continuous process.

Typically, the sequence used for converting PAN fibers into carbon fibers first begins by stretching the fibers in steam. The fibers are then heated to between 390°F and 570°F (200°C and 300°C) to make them more stable. The change to carbon takes place at a much higher temperature—at up to 1800°F (1000°C).

The carbonization heating stage is carried out in an atmosphere of inactive gas (a gas that does not cause a reaction), such as argon. During this heating process, the fibers shrink and give off various gases as they decompose. These gases include ammonia, carbon dioxide, water vapor, hydrogen cyanide, and nitrogen.

The final stage in the heat treatment is called graphitization, which involves heating the fibers to between 3600°F and 5400°F (2000°C to 3000°C). This produces a neat arrangement of graphite crystals in the fibers. (Graphite is the name of a certain crystalline form of carbon.) Graphitized carbon fibers are much stronger and stiffer than other types of the fiber.

Mixing for strength

To make full use of the strength of carbon fibers, they must be combined with another material called the matrix. This material may be a plastic, metal, or ceramic. The matrix is used to bind and protect the fibers, and the combination is called the composite (a composite is a mixture of materials).

The carbon fiber wheel of a sportsbike is made with carbon fiber cloth, vacuum baked with a matrix in a mold. The strength and light weight of carbon fiber make it ideal for many such high-tech applications.

When using a plastic matrix, such as epoxy resin, blocks or sheets of the composite can be formed by molding. The plastic is poured over the carbon fibers in a mold and allowed to set. Some fibers are specially treated to improve the bond with the resins. The surface may be pitted by allowing it to be attacked by a liquid or gas. Alternatively, chemical "whiskers" may be grown on the surface of the fibers. Both these techniques help the resin to grip the fibers and so increase the strength of the composite.

Besides being extremely strong and light, carbon fiber–reinforced plastics can resist attack from chemicals and can be used safely in many places where other materials, such as metals, would rust. They can also be made hard enough to use in bearings and gears.

To produce a composite suitable for use at very high temperatures, carbon fibers can be combined with metals or ceramics. The metal or ceramic is first ground into a very fine powder. It is then packed around the fibers, compressed, and heated. Carbon fibers can also be combined with metals using an electroplating process, in which the fibers are coated with metal by means of an electric current. Such high-temperature-resistant carbon fiber composites are used in space rockets, aircraft, engines, and other machine parts.

See also: CARBON • CERAMICS, INDUSTRIAL • ELECTROPLATING • PLASTIC

Casting

Making ice cubes is a simple example of casting. Water is poured into a shallow tray divided into small sections, called a mold. On cooling in a freezer, the water turns to ice. The ice blocks cast in this way are given their shape by the mold. Casting has been practiced for thousands of years, and beautiful ornaments cast in gold, silver, and bronze date from around 2500 BCE.

▲ Gold ingots are produced by casting gold. Many ingots are used for making jewelry. Also, as much as 45 percent of the world's gold is held by governments and central banks in ingots.

When copper and gold were first used to make jewelry about 8,000 years ago, hammering the metals was the only way known to give them shape. This was a hard, slow job and often left the metals brittle (easily broken). The idea of casting (pouring liquid metal into a mold for shaping) grew out of the new-found process of smelting (extracting metals from their parent rocks, or ores, by heating), about 4,500 years ago. In learning how to separate metals from their ores, people also learned that the metals would become liquid at a certain high temperature. If the metals were poured into molds when molten, they would set into the shape of the mold.

Casting meant that it was easier to form solid objects, such as tools and statues. Even better, as far as jewelry was concerned, was the fact that the inside of a mold could be decorated so that whatever was cast in it would be decorated as well.

The earliest molds for casting were made of stone, of which soapstone was the most popular. This soft stone was easy to cut and stood up well to the sudden heating that is created in casting.

A later material used for molds was sandy clay, which needed no cutting at all. Instead, damp clay was wrapped around a model of the object to be made. The cast was then carefully removed, repaired, and allowed to dry hard. The hardened clay held an impression of the shape wanted.

At first, casting was used mostly for small, flat, simple objects. It was hard to cut deep molds in stone, and although clay was easier to work, it was not strong enough for large casting. Also, both stone and clay wear out rather quickly when used over and over. So when the metal bronze came into wide use after 3000 BCE, stone and clay molds were largely replaced.

Bronze molds could be made as deep as necessary for a round object, such as an urn, or a bulky object, such as a statue. However, they had to be made in two pieces, with part of the mold in each half. These are known as piece molds and are still in use today, not only for metals, but also for decorative plaster, concrete, and plastics. The disadvantage of piece molds is that they never fit perfectly, so a thin trickle of metal, or whatever is being cast, usually squeezes out at the middle, making a seam.

About 4,000 years ago, the people of the Middle East devised another method of casting, known as lost-wax casting. First, they either made a model in wax or built wax up over a clay model. Several layers of sandy clay were put on over the wax, and the model was dried and fired like pottery. During the firing, the wax melted out of the clay, leaving a hollow mold with the shape impressed in its inside wall. Molten metal was then poured into the mold and allowed to harden by cooling.

▼ *Workers pour molten metal into large piece molds. The casts will be left to cool and harden before the molds are split apart and the casts removed. Factories where metal is melted and cast are known as foundries.*

MODERN CASTING

In modern manufacturing plants, metals and alloys (mixed metals) that have been melted to liquid are the substances poured into molds to cast hundreds of items used in the home and in industry. Since most molds can be used over and over, casting can turn out identical items in great quantities.

Casting is also carried out to change raw materials into a form that is easy to handle. For example, when a metal is extracted from its ore, it is often cast into blocks called ingots (the metal gold is an obvious example). Manufacturers use the

▲ *Liquid copper is being poured into molds at the Lubumbashi foundry in Congo. The copper casts, or ingots, will go to manufacturers, where the pure metal can be melted and turned into different products.*

ingots as raw material. The ingots may be melted for further casting or for a different use, or shaped in other ways, such as by grinding and cutting.

Even when a mold contains all the detail required in a product, some work has to be done on the castings to produce the finished item. For example, in a piece mold, the two parts that are held together while the material inside sets will form a ridge on the castings at the joint. This ridge has to be ground down after removal from the mold.

Sand casting

Sand casting is used to shape many materials. The products may weigh anything from a few grams up to several hundred tons. The sand used to make the molds is usually strengthened by adding clay or some other material. A model, or pattern, of an item is made out of wood or metal. It is then placed in a strong box, and the sand is compacted around it to form the mold.

A typical mold is made in two parts, so they can be separated and the pattern removed when the mold is formed. To make the casting, the mold pieces are held together and the melted (molten) metal, or other material, is poured into the mold through small openings in the sand. These openings, called sprues, cause projections on the hardened castings. These projections are cut off and the surface of the casting is smoothed.

Investment casting

Items of a very precise shape can be made by investment casting. Investment casting is a lost-wax process, because the wax, or other pattern material, is lost when the mold is made. The patterns, often made of wax or plastic, are themselves cast in a master mold called a die. Multiple patterns can therefore be made. The finished patterns are coated with chemicals or surrounded by compacted sand. Heat is then applied, and the patterns melt away, leaving hollow molds for casting.

Die casting

In die casting, liquid metal is injected under pressure into permanent metal molds. The technique is used for the mass production of cheap parts at high speed. A typical automobile has around 250 die-cast parts. Some simple die-cast items can be made on automatic machinery at the rate of hundreds per minute. In automatic die-casting machinery, cold water is circulated around the molds to cool the castings quickly.

See also: BLAST FURNACE • IRON AND STEEL • METALLURGY • METALWORKING

Catalyst

A chemical reaction takes place when two or more chemicals are mixed to produce a new substance. When the reaction involves making products, such as plastics, chemists often look to speed up the reaction to save time and money. To do this, another substance called a catalyst is added.

Although they might yield valuable products, many chemical reactions are too slow or do not even take place on their own. Chemists use catalysts to start or speed up these reactions. Most catalysts work by bringing the reactants closer together, in a position where they are more likely to react. An important property of catalysts is that they are not chemically altered during the reaction, so they can be used again and again.

A reaction that takes place with the aid of a catalyst is called a catalytic reaction. For example, heating a mixture of potassium chlorate ($KClO_3$) and manganese dioxide (MnO_2) produces oxygen gas (O_2) quicker than by heating potassium chlorate alone. The manganese dioxide speeds up the reaction, but it is left unchanged at the end. For this reason, the manganese dioxide does not appear in the chemical equation that shows what happens during the reaction.

▼ *In a petroleum plant, chemists use catalysts in a process called cracking. Catalytic cracking helps break down large petroleum molecules into smaller, more useful products such as gasoline.*

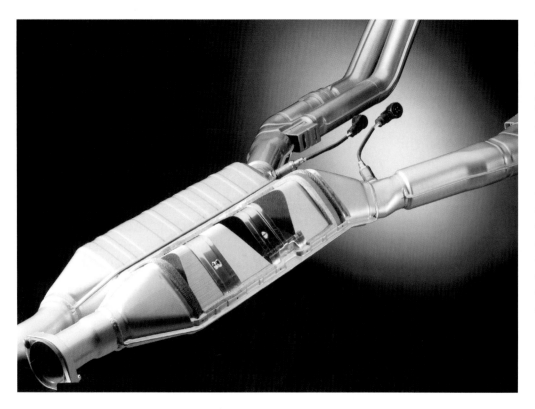

Catalytic converters change harmful gases in automobile exhaust fumes into less harmful gases. They help reduce the effects of air pollution in cities.

Inside a catalytic converter, a platinum and palladium catalyst converts hydrocarbons (substances containing carbon and hydrogen) and nitrogen oxides into carbon dioxide, nitrogen, oxygen, and water.

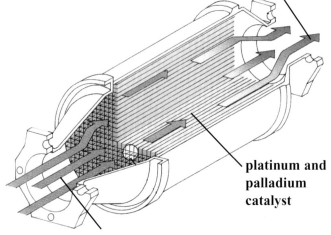

nitrogen, oxygen, carbon dioxide, and water

platinum and palladium catalyst

hydrocarbons and nitrogen oxides

Some catalysts can be used to slow down reactions. For example, a catalyst is often added to slow down the hardening of cement. This helps reduce the chance of the cement cracking.

Carrier and contact catalysts

Catalysts work in one of two ways. Carrier catalysts take part in reactions and form substances called intermediate compounds. These compounds then undergo reactions in which the catalysts are reformed. Contact catalysts have large porous surfaces on which the reactants "stick." Atoms or molecules of different substances collect on the surface of the catalyst, react, and then are released in a different form. Ammonia (NH_3) is made from nitrogen (N_2) and hydrogen (H_2) in this way.

The catalyst used in this example is impure iron, which is formed from the iron ore magnetite (Fe_3O_4). The surface atoms of the iron catalyst collect individual nitrogen (N) and hydrogen (H) atoms from molecules of nitrogen gas and oxygen gas. These atoms then combine in the ratio of three hydrogen atoms to each nitrogen atom to form molecules of ammonia. This gas is then released from the surface of the catalyst.

Biological catalysts

Enzymes are catalysts that speed up chemical reactions inside living organisms. Most enzymes are globular-shaped protein molecules, but other forms do exist. Every metabolic process is governed by the action of enzymes, from breaking down the food people eat to regulating the amount of sugar in the bloodstream.

See also: CHEMICAL REACTION • ENZYME

Cave

With their underground waterfalls and lakes, networks of passages and caverns, and strange formations such as stalactites and stalagmites, caves fascinate adventurers, explorers, and scientists alike. Caves are far from the warmth and light of the Sun, but they are home to unique animal life. Some caves have also been special places for people for tens of thousands of years.

▲ Stalactites and stalagmites line Harrison's Cave, Barbados, in the Caribbean. These unusual rock formations are created as mineral-rich water drips slowly through the roof and onto the floor of the cave.

A cave is any natural underground chamber large enough to admit a person. Artificial chambers, such as mines, are not caves because natural processes do not form them. Caves are carved out of the rock by a fluid that works itself beneath Earth's surface. Water is the fluid that usually forms caves.

Water can form caves in a number of ways. For example, rivers and streams can wear away the soft rock beneath a mass of overlying, harder rock, such as a granite bed lying in the bottom of a valley. Over time, the fast-flowing water will erode a channel through the soft rock, leaving an underground path beneath the granite. The so-called talus caves of California formed in this way. The sea can also wear away at soft rock beneath overlying harder rock, creating magnificent sea caves in the sides of cliffs.

Limestone caves

Most caves form by the action of water on rock called limestone (calcium carbonate; $CaCO_3$). Limestone always develops cracks through which water can trickle. Limestone also contains chemicals that are open to attack by acids. Rainwater is slightly acidic and reacts with the limestone, dissolving the rock and carrying it away as dissolved minerals.

Once underground, the water flows as a river or stream, seeping down through cracks in the limestone. The water dissolves the limestone, and the force of friction—and the sand and grit it contains—wears away the rock. Over time, the stream widens and deepens its channel through the limestone, forming a network of caverns and passages. The water often deposits the minerals it carries if it drips slowly from the roof of a cave. The deposited minerals form new rock in the shape of stalactites hanging down from the roof, and stalagmites growing up from the cave floor.

Later in the life of a cave system, the stream that created it might find a new course and leave the passages and caverns high and dry. In other cases, the sea level might rise relative to the land, and the cave will flood with seawater.

Lava tubes

Sometimes molten rock called lava is the fluid that forms caves. During a lava flow from a volcano, the surface lava cools first and freezes into solid rock.

DID YOU KNOW?

Earth's largest single cavern is the Sarawak Chamber in the Gua Payau Cave, Gunung Mulu National Park, Sarawak, Borneo. It is 1,980 feet (600 m) long, 1,320 feet (400 m) wide, and 330 feet (100 m) tall. It contains many cave swiftlets and more than one million bats of at least 12 different species.

Liquid lava continues to flow underneath, carving channels called lava tubes. When the lava flow stops, it often leaves empty tubes as caves. Caves formed by lava tubes can be found in Hawaii. Some are more than 40 miles (60 kilometers) long.

Damp and cold

The conditions inside most caves are cool and damp, and they change little from day to night and from summer to winter. The deeper inside a cave a person travels, the smaller the variation in temperature and moisture throughout the days and seasons. Conditions might seem stable, but dramatic changes can often occur if the stream flowing through a cave system floods. It may fill the cave system to the roof.

Life inside the caves

Many animals, from bears and mountains lions to snakes and spiders, use caves for shelter. Some of these animals move deep inside caves and rest there every day. Away from the entrance, a cave gradually becomes completely dark, so the animals that use the depths of caves find their way about by means other than eyesight. Cave birds, such as swiftlets in Southeast Asia and oilbirds in South America, make loud clicks and avoid the cave walls by listening for the echoes. This process is called echolocation. Swiftlets make cup-shaped nests and attach them to the cave wall with their saliva. These are the nests

▶ *Fruit bats cling to the walls of a cave in Bali. Bats roost in huge colonies inside caves. Their droppings feed entire communities of cave life, from cave crickets and cockroaches to cave spiders and centipedes.*

that people collect and use to make bird's nest soup. Oilbirds may travel up to 1 mile (1.6 kilometers) along cave passages to roost.

Bats, too, travel deep into caves to roost, using echolocation to navigate the cave system. They choose completely dark spots where predators will never find them. Bats also use the stable conditions inside caves for a long period of winter inactivity called hibernation. They choose a hibernation spot where the temperature is cold but never drops below freezing. In this way, bats use very little energy during hibernation, and they are in no danger of freezing solid.

Animals that spend their entire lives in caves may be found even deeper within the cave system. There is little to eat deep inside a cave, but if a stream flows through the cave system, it will bring with it a steady trickle of dead animal and plant material. Most animals that spend their entire lives in caves lack eyes. Some species have no pigment (color chemicals) in their skin. Pigments usually shield an animal from the Sun and may also provide camouflage against predators or a display to other

members of the species. Since they live in darkness, cave animals have little use for pigments. They manage to survive on a meager diet by being generally inactive and growing very slowly.

The animals are very different in caves flooded by the sea, but most animals in sea caves are also very inactive and slow growing. Animals of sea caves include strange creatures that seem to be relics of the past, such as sponges with huge, stony skeletons and primitive relatives of shrimps called remipedes.

Although caves can be harsh environments, they support complex food chains like any other environment. Microorganisms feed on dead material in the cave. Grazing on these microscopic life-forms are small invertebrates (animals without backbones), including tiny relatives of woodlice called isopods. Eating these small creatures are blind cave fish, such as the Ozark cave fish, and several species of cave salamanders, such as the Texas blind salamander and the olm.

The attraction of caves

People are drawn to caves for different reasons. Cavers enjoy the challenge of exploring complex cave systems. In the United States, cavers have discovered an incredible 350 miles (570 kilometers) of passages in Kentucky's Mammoth Cave system. As they went deeper into the caves, they found out that they were connected to the nearby Pine Ridge system, making the combined system of caves by far the longest known on Earth.

Other people visit caves to study the animals and people that use and live in them. Some caves are ideal sheltered places to preserve the remains of Earth's previous inhabitants. Dead bodies and bones are sometimes washed into caves, where they stay until they are discovered by fossil hunters. Scientists called paleontologists study the evidence of creatures of the past that used caves for shelter and for places to rest and feed. Paleontologists have discovered remains of the extinct giant ground sloth of South America and the extinct cave bear of Europe. They have also discovered some important facts about the life of early humans from their exploration of caves. For example, they have found

▲ *The entrance to this cave has been flooded by the stream that formed it, and expert cave divers have been sent to explore it.*

evidence of people fishing in the sea as long as 100,000 years ago from fish bones and artifacts found in a South African cave.

Cave painting

Perhaps the best record of human activity in caves is cave art. Right up to the present day, people have painted and carved on cave walls throughout the world. Some cave paintings, such as those in Altamira in Spain and Lascaux and Chauvet in France, are more than 30,000 years old. They offer unique insights into what early humans thought about their environment. Many paintings depict animals that lived at the time, so cave paintings are invaluable for zoologists seeking information about the ancestors of present-day species.

There are lots of ancient paintings in caves, but this does not mean that early people lived in caves or even spent much time in them. They probably found caves too cold and damp and may have lived in huts or tents outside. They may have created art everywhere, but the ideal conditions inside caves, away from the wind and rain, have preserved their paintings there to the present day.

See also: BIOMES AND HABITATS

Cell

Cells are the basic building blocks of all living organisms. Some animals and plants consist of just one single cell. Most are made up of billions of cells.

English scientist Robert Hooke (1635–1703) was the first person to talk about cells. In 1665, Hooke published a book in which he described looking at a thin slice of cork under a light microscope he had just built. Hooke noted that the cork slice consisted of many tiny, boxlike units. He called each one a cell, because they reminded him of the cells of a monastery. Less than 20 years later, Dutch scientist Anthony van Leeuwenhoek (1632–1723) became the first person to look at a living cell under his own microscope.

Modern biologists know a lot about the structure and function of cells. They can look at cells in great detail using powerful electron microscopes. Instead of using light to look at tiny objects, these instruments use waves of negatively charged particles called electrons. Using electron microscopes, biologists have discovered some important chemicals found inside cells. They have also figured out what these chemicals do.

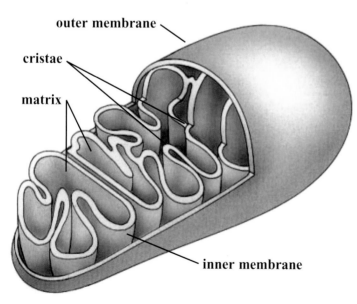

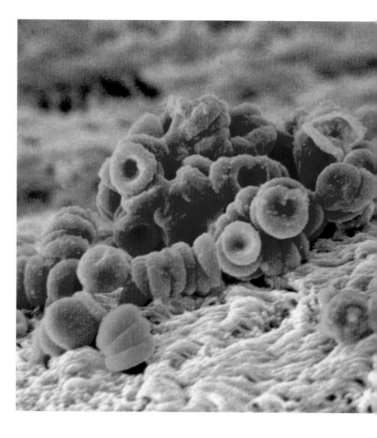

▲ Red blood cells gather on the wall of an artery. One drop of blood contains about 300 million red blood cells. Their main job is to transport oxygen from the lungs and deliver it to other cells in the body.

Shapes and sizes

Cells come in many different shapes and sizes. Human red blood cells measure just a tiny fraction of an inch across. They look like flattened disks, but they can change shape to squeeze through tiny blood vessels. The largest known cell in the animal kingdom is the yolk of an ostrich egg. It weighs about 3 pounds (1.4 kilograms). The nerve cells in the spinal cord of a giraffe take the prize for the world's longest cells. One cell may measure up to 2 feet (0.6 meters) in length.

◄ The energy-producing mitochondrion has a double membrane. The outer membrane encloses the mitochondrion. The inner membrane is folded into cristae that increase the surface area of the mitochondrion. This folding produces a matrix that houses DNA and enzymes involved in cell metabolism.

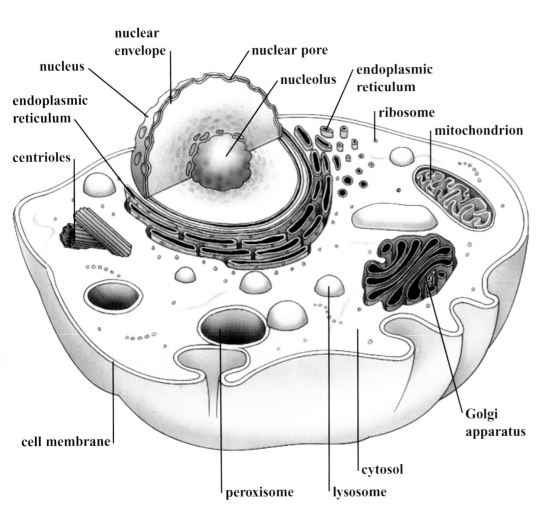

nuclear envelope
nuclear pore
nucleus
nucleolus
endoplasmic reticulum
endoplasmic reticulum
ribosome
mitochondrion
centrioles
cell membrane
peroxisome
lysosome
cytosol
Golgi apparatus

◄ Animal cells are enclosed by a protective cell membrane. Inside the membrane is a watery fluid called cytosol. At the center is the cell's nucleus, which houses genetic material in the form of DNA. Ribosomes are made in the nucleolus and pass out of the nuclear envelope through the endoplasmic reticulum. Protein is made from amino acids in the ribosomes. In the mitochondrion, sugar and oxygen are made into energy. All these chemical reactions produce waste products, which leave through the cell membrane. Some are broken down by peroxisomes and lysosomes and expelled through the Golgi apparatus. The centrioles regulate cell division.

Inside the cell

Whatever their shape or size, all cells consist of a cell membrane and protoplasm. The cell membrane is the "skin" of the cell, protecting it from the outside world. The protoplasm is everything inside the cell membrane—the nucleus and the cytoplasm. The nucleus is the cell's "brain." It contains the organism's genetic blueprint and directs the various chemical changes that keep the cell alive. The cytoplasm is all the other parts of the cell, including the watery fluid, called cytosol, in which all the internal parts of the cell are suspended.

The cell membrane

The cell membrane is a thin, tough envelope consisting of a layer of protein and fat molecules that hold the cell together. Biologists think that the cell membrane has tiny pores through which small molecules can pass. It allows useful molecules to pass through, but it rejects harmful molecules. The cell membrane also forces out the waste products of cell metabolism. Larger molecules may pass through the membrane by means of diffusion or a process called pinocytosis. Diffusion occurs when chemicals in the cell membrane dissolve the large molecules so that they can pass through the membrane. Pinocytosis occurs when the cell membrane engulfs molecules floating in the fluid surrounding the cell.

Cytosol and cell organelles

Water is the main component of cytosol. It makes up between 60 and 95 percent of the total volume. Mixed in this water are carbohydrates, fat molecules, proteins, and several structures called organelles. One important cell process takes place inside tiny organelles called mitochondria. The mitochondria act as power generators for the cell.

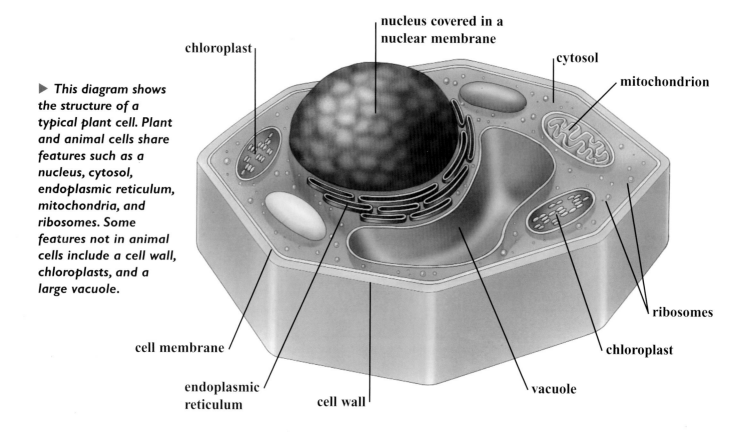

chloroplast

nucleus covered in a nuclear membrane

cytosol

mitochondrion

▶ *This diagram shows the structure of a typical plant cell. Plant and animal cells share features such as a nucleus, cytosol, endoplasmic reticulum, mitochondria, and ribosomes. Some features not in animal cells include a cell wall, chloroplasts, and a large vacuole.*

cell membrane

endoplasmic reticulum

cell wall

vacuole

chloroplast

ribosomes

Sugar and dissolved oxygen react inside the mitochondria, producing energy and carbon dioxide. This energy is used to power other cell processes. The carbon dioxide is released as waste.

Proteins are some of the main products of cells. They consist of chains of chemicals called amino acids, which are found floating in the cytosol. Some proteins are very long chains of amino acids folded up into complex shapes. The jobs they do often depend on their shapes. Proteins are manufactured on tiny organelles called ribosomes.

Some of the chemical reactions in cells produce very useful proteins called enzymes, which help the growth and repair of many different cells. Enzymes made in one cell often have to be transported to other cells in an organism. The Golgi apparatus is the mechanism that allows enzymes to pass from cell to cell. Waste products also pass out of the cell through the Golgi apparatus, after being broken down by organelles called lysosomes.

There are many other organelles in the cytoplasm. Vacuoles drift through the cytosol carrying food molecules. Vacuoles also appear to regulate the amount of water in single-celled animals such as amoebas. Plastids are common organelles in the cytoplasm of plants and single-celled animals. Plastids store food and other chemicals. In plant cells, plastids called chloroplasts store a chemical called chlorophyll. Plants use this chemical to produce energy from sunlight.

The nucleus

At the center of the cell lies the nucleus, which controls cell division and growth. This dense structure contains the genetic blueprint for life in the form of long strands of deoxyribonucleic acid (DNA) floating in a liquid called nucleoplasm. Specific sequences of DNA, known as genes, are the units of heredity in most organisms. DNA also controls the production of proteins by regulating

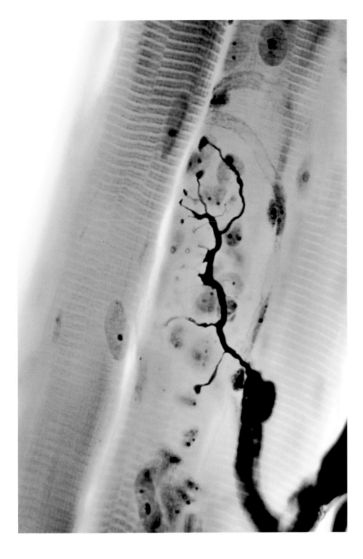

▲ *The end of a motor nerve fiber connects to muscle fibers at a point called the motor end plate. Motor nerves transmit information from the central nervous system to muscles, which contract and move the body.*

the production of an intermediate chemical called ribonucleic acid (RNA). Biologists believe that RNA is made and then stored in a nuclear structure called the nucleolus. It stays there until it is needed to make new proteins.

Cell division

There are two different forms of cell division. Mitosis is the process by which one cell splits into two identical cells, or daughter cells. Before the cell divides, the thin DNA strands in the nucleus form rodlike structures called chromosomes. Each chromosome then splits into an identical pair of chromosomes, which line up along the midpoint of

the cell. As the cell starts to divide along the midpoint, identical chromosomes move in opposite directions. The cell membrane then pinches in around each set of chromosomes. Each daughter cell therefore receives one chromosome from the identical pair, so the final cells are also identical. Biologists have found out that organelles called centrioles found near the nucleus help direct each chromosome from the identical pair toward one of the new daughter cells.

Meiosis is another type of cell division. Meiosis produces male and female sex cells—the male sperm and female egg—with only half the number of chromosomes characteristic of the organism. Normal human cells contain 46 chromosomes, for example, but the sex cells contain only 23 chromosomes. When the sperm and egg meet during fertilization, the full set of 46 chromosomes is restored—half from each parent. In this way, the offspring inherits characteristics from each parent.

Cell communication

Some organisms consist of just one cell. Amoebas, bacteria, and some algae are examples of single-celled organisms. Other living things consist of billions of different cells all working together. Specialized cells form the different parts of a plant, such as the flowers and fruits. The human body contains many different cells, from neurons in the brain to lymphocytes (white blood cells) in the bloodstream.

Different cells must communicate to keep the entire organism alive. They do this by releasing chemical messengers. Hormones are one kind of messenger. They are released by one cell and travel in the blood to another cell. Neurotransmitters are another kind of messenger. They are released by nerve cells to signal nearby nerve cells or to signal muscle cells to contract or relax.

When a messenger reaches a target cell, it usually attaches to a "receptor" on the cell membrane. The receptor is a protein that extends all the way through the membrane. The outer end has a shape that exactly fits the shape of one particular messenger molecule. The inner end reacts with cell chemicals called effectors.

▲ *Erwin Neher (top) and Bert Sakmann (above) were awarded the 1991 Nobel Prize for physiology or medicine for discovering how one type of ion channel works. They did this using a technique called patch clamping.*

How receptors work

When a messenger molecule binds to a receptor, it sometimes changes the shape of that receptor. This is rather like the way in which squeezing one end of a long balloon changes the shape of the other end of the balloon. This change makes the part of the receptor on the inside of the cell the right shape to react with the effector. Some other kinds of receptors carry the messenger molecule right through the membrane and release it inside. Still others form a channel that opens or closes when a messenger binds to the receptor. An open or closed channel determines whether or not other chemicals can flow into or out of the cell. These receptors, or "ion channels," generate the tiny electric currents that carry signals along nerve fibers. When an ion channel is closed, it does not let positively charged ions enter the cell. (Ions are atoms that have gained or lost electrons, so they have an electric charge.) A negative charge is thus created inside the cell, generating an electrical signal. When one nerve cell signals another by releasing a neurotransmitter, the neurotransmitter often causes an ion channel to close, so that the second nerve cell sends an electrical signal along its nerve fiber.

Ion channels in vision

Ion channels translate light into electrical signals in the eyes. Cells in the retina of the eye (the part on which the lens focuses light) contain a chemical called rhodopsin. When light strikes the rhodopsin, it activates another chemical called transducin. This second chemical causes ion channels in the cell membrane to close, sending an electrical signal along the optic nerve to the brain. The advantage of the extra step is that one rhodopsin molecule can activate more than 500 transducin molecules, so even a very dim light can generate a signal.

Scientists have discovered that many kinds of cells use multistep systems, such as the ion channels in vision, to translate a signal from a receptor into action. This discovery has shed much light on several diseases. For example, defects in some signaling proteins in a cell can lead to uncontrolled cell growth, or cancer. Defective signaling proteins have been found in cancer cells and in people with diabetes and some other diseases. This research may eventually lead to drugs that work just on the damaged proteins, correcting diseased cells while leaving healthy cells untouched.

Patch clamping

One technique that has led to important discoveries in cell biology is called patch clamping. Patch clamping is done with a thin glass tube called a pipette. The tip of the pipette, which measures just a tiny fraction of the width of a human hair, is tightly sealed against a cell membrane. This encloses a small patch of the membrane and the ion channels on it. Biologists can then apply stimuli from within the pipette and measure the behavior of the trapped channels. If the membrane patch can be pierced without breaking the seal between the pipette and the membrane, biologists can also study the inside of the cell through the pipette.

From egg to organism

How does a single egg cell develop into a complex organism made up of billions of cells? After fertilization, the egg cell divides again and again, forming a mass of cells called an embryo. Some cells become bone, others muscle, others skin, and so on. How does each cell know what to be?

Biologists may have found the answer. The clue came from fruit flies. When certain genes in the flies were damaged, their offspring were deformed. Some had extra wings. Others had legs growing out of their heads. The damaged genes had to be ones that told cells what to become. They were named "Hox genes." Biologists believe Hox genes are present in every animal, including people.

No one knows for sure what triggers the Hox genes, but they start in just the right order to create each section of the embryo at the right time and place. Biologists think that they may be activated by a higher concentration of chemicals in a particular part of the embryo. Hox genes in the cells in that area then code for proteins called "transcription factors." These proteins attach to DNA in the nucleus of the cells and turn on other genes. Then

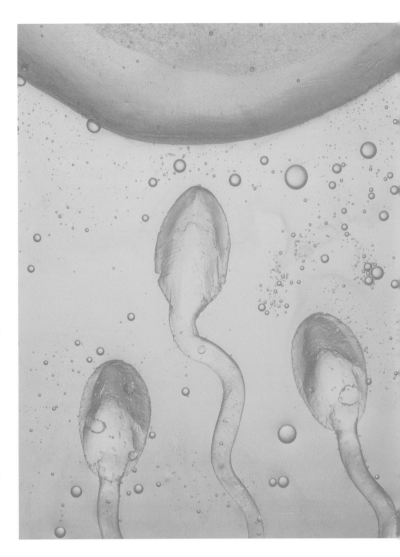

▲ *Free-swimming sperm cells approach a human egg, called an ovum. Fertilization occurs when a sperm cell penetrates the ovum's cell membrane. The nuclei of the ovum and sperm cells then merge to form an embryo.*

those genes direct the cells to do a job. In this way, the cells in each small region of the embryo eventually develop into a particular organ or tissue.

There are still many unanswered questions in this field of biology, called embryology. However, understanding how the human body develops may help prevent birth defects and cure many diseases that occur as people grow older, such as arthritis, cancer, and heart disease.

See also: AMINO ACID • BACTERIA • BIOCHEMISTRY • CLONING • DNA • ENZYME • GENETICS • METABOLISM • PHOTOSYNTHESIS • PROTEIN

Centrifuge

A washing machine is a form of centrifuge. During its spin-dry cycle the drum spins so fast that water is forced out of the wet clothes. This same type of force (or power) is also applied to many other uses. Centrifuges are used extensively in industry and in scientific laboratories to separate solutions into their constituent parts.

A centrifuge is a machine that rotates to produce an outward, or centrifugal, force. This action is often used to separate solids from liquids, or to separate two liquids. A washing machine running a spin-dry cycle is an example of a centrifuge that separates a liquid (the water in the clothes) from solids (the clothes). The drum containing the wet clothes spins rapidly, and centrifugal force pushes the clothes against the outside of the drum. Holes in the drum allow the water to pass through. At the end of the cycle, the clothes are partly dry and are ready to be completely dried by the heat of a dryer.

Similar machines are used in the food, chemical, and mineral industries to remove water from many kinds of solids, such as sugar, starch, and fine coal.

Solids can also be separated from liquids by filtering. However, filtering fine particles from a liquid is a slow process because the liquid has to be passed through a material with extremely fine holes. The particles are trapped while the liquid drips through. The advantage of using a centrifuge is that it can make the separation so much faster. The quicker it spins, the greater the centrifugal force produced and the faster the separation.

Some commercial centrifuges work with batches. Like domestic spin dryers, they have to be loaded, operated, and unloaded. Others are designed so that the substances to be separated can be passed through continuously. The two main types of continuous centrifuge are called pushers and separators.

▲ *Samples are being prepared and loaded into a laboratory centrifuge. The centrifuge separates many of the components of a substance, aiding analysis.*

Pushers

The pusher centrifuge has a plate that moves back and forth. It pushes out the drained solids which then can be collected without stopping the machine. Some pusher centrifuges also wash the separated solids. Machines of this type are widely used in the chemical industry to wash and collect crystals after separation.

The decanter centrifuge is similar to the pusher type, but it uses a different method for removing the solids. Instead of a moving plate, a screw conveyor is used. A screw conveyor is a large, revolving spindle with a spiral ridge wound around it, so that it looks like a giant screw. As the machine turns, the solids are steadily "screwed" out of the centrifuge in a semi-dry state. Decanter centrifuges are often used to remove water from sewer wastes.

▶ *This type of ultracentrifuge is typical of those used to separate individual particles within cells. Larger particles such as cell nuclei separate out at lower speeds, with smaller particles requiring higher speeds. The tubes containing the samples are placed in holes in a solid block of metal, the rotor, which whirls around at high speed, powered by an electric motor. A vacuum pump removes air from around the rotor to reduce friction. The casing of the centrifuge includes protective armor so that if the rotor should become loose it will not fly across the laboratory. There is also a refrigeration system to keep the samples cool.*

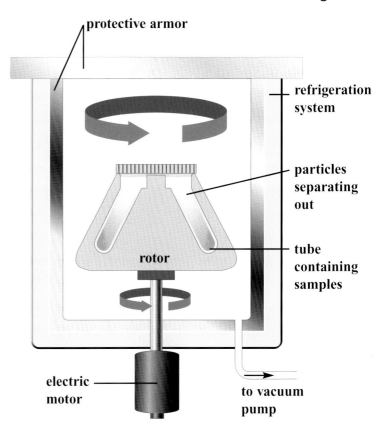

protective armor

refrigeration system

particles separating out

tube containing samples

rotor

electric motor

to vacuum pump

Separators

In a continuous separator centrifuge, the mixture to be separated is pumped into a bowl that turns at high speed. The heavier part of the mixture is collected from the edge of the bowl, while the lighter part is obtained from the center.

The first continuous separator was developed in Sweden in the 1880s to separate cream from milk. Today such machines are also used to remove impurities from lubricating oils and the sediment from wines and beers.

Ultracentrifuges

The fastest spinning centrifuges turn at more than 20,000 revolutions per minute. These machines, called ultracentrifuges, are used by scientists to study the large molecules of substances such as polymers and proteins. The weight of a molecule can be worked out from the way the substance behaves in the ultracentrifuge.

G-forces

The strength of the outward force produced by a centrifuge is often expressed in terms of Earth's force of gravity (g-force) because it is a similar to gravity and causes similar effects. Suppose, for example, that you leave a jar of muddy water to stand. The force of gravity will gradually cause the heavier parts of the mixture to settle at the bottom. A centrifuge can produce a force much stronger than that of gravity, so it would be able to separate the mixture much more quickly. Commercial centrifuges can produce a force up to about 2,000 times that of gravity. This is sometimes called a g-force of 2,000. In an ultracentrifuge, the g-force may reach 2,000,000.

◀ *A centrifuge is being used for testing at a NASA research facility in California. Due to the rapid acceleration of a rocket or space shuttle during its launch, large g-forces are created, so it is necessary to test some parts of spacecraft to see how they react. Even astronauts are trained in large centrifuges to enable them to get used to the stresses of launch.*

See also: GRAVITY

Ceramics, industrial

Bricks, dinner plates, and parts of the space shuttle have one thing in common. They are all made from materials called ceramics. The word *ceramic* comes from the Greek word *keramikos,* meaning "of pottery," because pots and vases were among the first ceramic items made.

Ceramics are traditionally made by heating shaped clay. The important quality of ceramics is their great strength. Ceramics are generally harder than metals, so they make useful abrasives for shaping or grinding other materials.

Although ceramics are brittle and may crack under tension, they can withstand extremely high pressure, even at temperatures close to their melting point. This makes them useful for holding very hot substances, lining ovens and furnaces, and for use on spacecraft. Space shuttles, for example, use advanced ceramic tiles on their underside as heat resistors because an enormous amount of heat is generated when the shuttle re-enters Earth's atmosphere from space.

Ceramics are also highly resistant to wear, even if they come in contact with hot or strong chemicals. They are, therefore, widely used for holding liquid metals, acids, and alkalis. Ceramics are also used as electrical insulators because they do not conduct electricity very well.

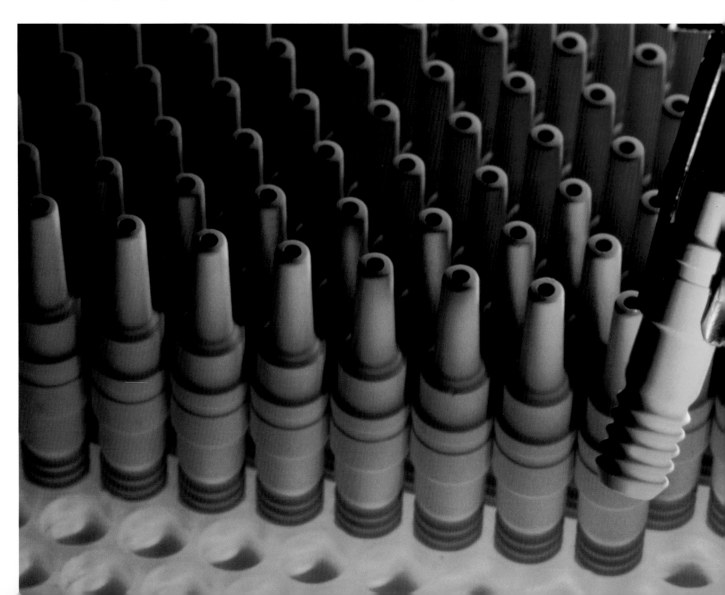

▶ *Here, special ceramic tiles are being fixed on the underside of the space shuttle **Atlantis**. These will resist the ultrahigh temperatures generated when the spacecraft re-enters Earth's atmosphere and will prevent the shuttle from burning up.*

▼ *Automobile spark plugs have ceramic coverings. Ceramic is a good insulator and is used widely in the electronics industry.*

Heavy clay products

These products include building materials such as bricks, roof tiles, floor tiles, and sewerage pipes. The raw materials used to make heavy-clay products vary from place to place, depending on the kind of clay or shale (a flaky rock made of clay) available locally. After the products have been shaped, they are fired (heated in a furnace) at between 1652°F and 2012°F (900°C and 1100°C) to give them the necessary strength. Special firing techniques have been developed to manufacture bricks that can withstand the immense forces of pressure in the structures of tall buildings.

Modern ceramics

In the last few decades, new ceramics have been developed using different substances from clay. These have been created, along with the new techniques needed to make them, to meet the needs of modern industry. Some of these new ceramic substances are made by refining natural materials, such as metal ores (rocks containing a large proportion of a metal). Others, such as barium titanate, silicon nitride, and silicon carbide, are made by chemical processes.

Ceramics such as boron nitride, boron carbide, zirconium boride, and silicon carbide are used when the ability to withstand extremely high temperatures is needed. Zirconium boride is also used for coating turbine blades and brake and clutch linings. Nuclear fuels are usually made from thoria, urania, or uranium carbide. Some ceramics show a piezoelectric effect—when the material is bent, it produces an electrical charge. This effect is used in some electronic watches, microphones, and electronic cigarette lighters. Piezoelectric ceramics include lead zirconate titanate (known as PZT) and barium titanate. Hard-wearing ceramics, such as alumina, zirconium boride, and silicon nitride, are used in bearings.

Alumina and silicon carbide (commonly called carborundum) are used for grinding powders and abrasives. Alumina is mixed with a form of iron oxide to make the abrasive called emery. Alumina is also used to make automobile spark plugs. Magnesia, zirconia, and thoria are high-temperature (refractory) materials used to make crucibles and furnace elements. In electronics, titania is widely used in capacitors. The magnetic ceramics called ferrites have many applications including transformer cores, antenna rods, and permanent magnets.

Glass ceramics

In some glasses it is possible to produce a certain degree of crystallization in the normally random atomic structure. Glassy materials with such a structure are called glass ceramics. Normal glass is a strong material, but its random structure weakens it, and any flaws (faults) in it tend to cause cracks. To produce a glass ceramic with a strong structure

◄ *Automobile windshields are being checked and finished before fitting. They are made from strong glass ceramic, which is much stronger than ordinary glass. This material has greatly improved the safety of automobiles.*

◄ *Ceramics, reinforced with carbon fiber, are used to make high-performance brake discs. These discs can withstand the large forces and very high temperatures generated by racing cars and large trucks better than ordinary brake discs.*

expansion. The stresses caused by this expansion can crack the glass. Glass ceramics with low expansion will not crack when heated.

Making ceramic products

Ceramic products can be made by molding, plastic forming, or casting. Usually, the raw materials are first ground to the correct particle size and mixed with water. In molding, for example, a plate, some of the water is removed to leave a plastic paste, which is pressed onto a mold to form the plate. After drying, the plate is fired in a kiln. It is then glazed and decorated and returned to the kiln for further firings to develop the colors.

Cups, bowls, and similar objects are made by plastic forming or casting. In plastic forming, the plastic paste is shaped by hand, potter's wheel, or other machinery. In the casting process, a porous mold is used. The raw materials are in the form of a suspension in water. This mixture is poured into the mold, which absorbs the liquid. The solids are, therefore, left on the walls of the mold. This process is repeated until the solid layer is sufficiently thick. The casting is then dried, separated from the mold, and fired and glazed.

Tiles are made by pressing dry powdered material into a die of the required shape. The shaped powder is removed from the die, dried, fired, and then glazed and decorated. Most of the modern ceramic materials are formed by dry pressing techniques that were developed from tile pressing.

In isostatic pressing, the powdered materials are placed in a die. The die is put into a pliable bag made of rubber, plastic, or metal. The bag is surrounded by a liquid, which produces an even pressure around the die. After pressing, the material is removed from the die, trimmed, dried, and fired.

of microscopic crystals that is free of pores (tiny gaps, which weaken a material), the glass is subjected to a controlled heating cycle at very high temperatures—up to 3092°F (1700°C).

Different types of glass ceramics can be made by changing the composition of the original glass. A glass ceramic made with a capacity for electrical insulation is used in electronic components. A type with very low expansion can be produced for ovenware. This type is made from pure silica. In ordinary glass, uneven heating causes uneven

See also: ABRASIVE • GLASS

Chaos theory

When people talk about chaos they usually describe total disorganization, with no order or pattern. However, the aim of chaos theory is to find order where there seems to be none at all. People now use chaos theory to explain natural events that appear to be quite random.

Chaos theory is a branch of science that deals with the nature of chaotic systems. Many natural events, such as the movement of molecules in a boiling liquid, can be described by well-known physical laws and seem very simple. However, these systems often behave in a random and unpredictable way. Chaos theory tries to make accurate long-term predictions about the behavior of such events.

Understanding chaos theory

It was not until computers became fast and powerful that chaos theory could be studied properly. A good example of chaos theory in action is in weather forecasting. There are huge numbers of factors that can affect the weather across the world. Yet it is possible to work out mathematical equations that show, for example, how heating the land in one place causes wind to blow in another. This process is called making a model of the weather. Mathematicians can then draw a graph of the way the different factors vary with each other. The result is a striking butterfly-shaped figure called Lorenz's Strange Attractor.

Following the line of this figure shows that only a slight change in the starting position can make a huge difference in the end result. In other words, it is like saying that a butterfly flapping its wings in Brazil could set off a tornado in Texas. The small

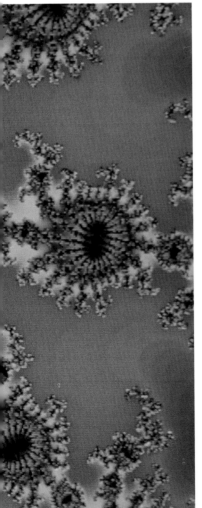

▲ On the trading floor of the New York Stock Exchange, a huge number of transactions take place daily. People use chaos theory to study events that are effectively impossible to predict, such as the long-term fluctuations in the price of stocks and shares.

◄ The illustration at left is a computer-generated representation of part of a complex graph called the Mandelbrot set. This is an example of fractal geometry, which can be used to describe order or the presence of patterns in apparently chaotic systems, such as chemical reactions or the weather.

change in wind patterns around the butterfly can alter larger wind patterns which, in turn, have greater effects. In the real world, millions of variables affect the weather, making accurate predictions nearly impossible.

Chaos in the skies

In 1992, chaos theory helped two scientists at Sussex University, Britain, explain why auroras occur. Auroras are caused by highly charged solar particles colliding with oxygen and nitrogen atoms in Earth's upper atmosphere. The particles can make the oxygen and nitrogen atoms glow with brilliant colors over the polar regions. Auroras are very hard to predict. The scientists found that when conditions are right, the atoms in Earth's magnetic fields can rapidly change from having a regular motion to having a chaotic motion. This finding helps explain why auroras start so suddenly.

See also: MATHEMATICS • NUMBER SYSTEM

Chemical reaction

A chemical reaction converts one set of substances, called the reactants, into another set of substances, called the products. Chemical reactions occur in nature, in laboratories, and in industry.

Nuclear processes cause chemical changes in a different way from chemical reactions. During a nuclear change, an atom of one element becomes an atom of a different element. This change occurs because the dense nucleus at the center of the atom gains or loses one or more particles. Some nuclear changes happen naturally, but scientists can also force nuclear changes to occur in a nuclear reactor.

Laboratory reactions

When a chemical reaction happens in nature, there are often many substances present, which makes it difficult to know for certain how the reaction works. Several different reactions can also happen at the same time. In laboratories, chemists simplify their studies by mixing together known quantities of pure substances and observing how they react. The starting materials—the substances that react—are called the reactants. The substances left after the reaction has occurred are called the products. Studies of laboratory reactions help chemists

◀ *Firework explosions are caused by energetic chemical reactions involving gunpowder and substances that make distinctive noises and produce colored flames when they burn.*

Chemical reactions are going on all the time. They occur whenever a candle burns, a firework explodes, or a piece of scrap metal rusts. Chemical reactions contribute to the growth and decay of plants, the formation and erosion of rocks, and the life processes of people and animals.

Chemical reactions are an example of how matter changes from one form to another. Chemical reactions change how atoms group together to form compounds. Other changes are physical or nuclear. During physical changes, the chemical compounds remain the same, but they change in physical state. Melting and boiling are examples of physical changes. Melting changes substances from solids to liquids. Boiling changes them from liquids to gases.

DID YOU KNOW?

Jöns Jakob Berzelius came up with the modern system of chemical symbols and formulas in 1811. Many chemical symbols are shortened forms of the chemical name in English. For example, *Ba* stands for barium and *O* stands for oxygen. Other symbols come from Latin names. The symbol for the metal lead, *Pb*, comes from the Latin word *plumbum*. Numbers after symbols indicate how many atoms of that element are in the compound. For example, water (H_2O) has two atoms of hydrogen attached to one atom of oxygen.

Magnesium burns in air with a brilliant white flame to form a mixture of white magnesium oxide (MgO) and magnesium nitride (Mg_3N_2).

understand how reactions occur in nature. They also help chemists find ways of making new chemical compounds.

Chemists seldom start from scratch in the laboratory, since they can read about many of the reactions they need in books and from the reports of other chemists. On the other hand, when a research chemist discovers a reaction that nobody else has reported, he or she can publish the findings so that other chemists can be aware of the new reaction. In this way, the wealth of chemical knowledge has grown over past centuries and will continue to do so in the future. The reporting system relies on a universal system of symbols introduced in the nineteenth century by Swedish chemist Jöns Jakob Berzelius (1779–1848).

Following the rules

A few simple rules help chemists figure out what goes on during chemical reactions. The first rule states that a chemical reaction neither creates nor destroys matter. In other words, the numbers and types of atoms before the reaction must be the same as the numbers and types of atoms after the reaction. The atoms simply join up in different combinations to form new molecules. With this in mind, chemists write balanced equations to account for all the atoms before the reaction and all the atoms after the reaction. An example is the equation for the reaction of hydrochloric acid (HCl) with calcium carbonate ($CaCO_3$), which produces calcium chloride ($CaCl_2$), carbon dioxide gas (CO_2), and water (H_2O). The reaction that takes place can be written like this:

$$CaCO_3 + 2HCl \rightarrow CaCl_2 + CO_2 + H_2O$$

It is impossible to count directly the atoms that take part in the reaction, since they are far too numerous and small. Instead, chemists measure the masses of the reactants and products. They do this by multiplying the numbers of each type of atom by its relative atomic mass (RAM). For the example of hydrochloric acid and calcium carbonate, this is done as follows (see the box below to find out the RAM of each element involved in the reaction):

$$CaCO_3 + 2HCl \rightarrow CaCl_2 + CO_2 + H_2O$$

$40 + 12 + (3 \times 16)$	$2 \times (1 + 35.5)$	$40 + (2 \times 35.5)$	$12 + (2 \times 16)$	$(2 \times 1) + 16$
100	**73**	**111**	**44**	**18**

From this equation, chemists know that 100 grams of calcium carbonate will react with 73 grams of hydrogen chloride (contained in a water solution of hydrochloric acid) to produce 111 grams of calcium chloride and 44 grams of carbon dioxide. Chemists do not include the mass of the water because of the water content of the acid.

DID YOU KNOW?

Element	Chemical symbol	RAM
Calcium	Ca	40
Carbon	C	12
Oxygen	O	16
Hydrogen	H	1
Chlorine	Cl	35.5

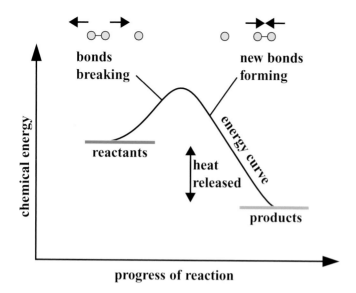

bonds
breaking

new bonds
forming

chemical energy

reactants

energy curve

heat
released

products

progress of reaction

▲ Chemists use diagrams like this one to show the changes in energy during a chemical reaction. This diagram shows an exothermic reaction. The hump in the energy curve of the reactants' molecules is an energy barrier that molecules have to clear if they are to react.

The second rule of chemical reactions states that energy can neither be created nor destroyed. In the case of the reaction between hydrochloric acid and calcium carbonate, the reaction mixture gets warmer as the reaction proceeds. This shows that the heat energy of the mixture increases. This energy comes from chemical energy locked up in the starting materials.

The chemical energy of a compound depends on the bonds that hold its atoms together. For a molecule of two atoms, this force behaves in a similar way to the attraction between two horseshoe magnets with their opposite poles touching. To separate the magnets requires an effort; in a similar way, it takes an input of energy to break the bond and separate the atoms of the molecule. In reverse, the formation of a bond releases energy in the form of heat.

In an exothermic reaction, the energy content of the products is less than that of the reactants, and heat is given out during the reaction. In an endothermic reaction, the reverse is true. In this case, the energy content of the products is more than that of the reactants, and heat is taken in during the reaction.

What makes a reaction occur?

Some reactions happen as soon as the reactants are mixed at room temperature. Others need a helping hand to get going. An example is the reaction of gasoline with air. Left alone, no reaction happens at room temperature. Given a spark, however, gasoline catches fire and can even explode. Why does this happen?

The energy diagram to the left gives a clue as to why some reactions occur on their own and others need a kick start. The first part of any reaction requires energy to break bonds and get over the hump in the energy curve. In some cases, the heat energy that the reactants have at room temperature is enough to get over the hump, so the reaction goes ahead as soon as the reactants are mixed.

In other cases, the heat energy of reactant molecules is too little to clear the hump in the energy curve. The ignition spark of a gasoline engine provides enough heat to get a few gasoline molecules to react. Their reaction then releases

DID YOU KNOW?

The mass of an atom depends on the number of particles in its nucleus. The hydrogen atom is the lightest of all the chemical elements. It contains a single particle, called a proton, in its nucleus.

A carbon atom has 12 particles in its nucleus, so each carbon atom has 12 times the mass of a hydrogen atom. Chemists say that the relative atomic masses of hydrogen and carbon are 1 and 12, respectively.

A mole is the quantity of atoms of an element whose mass in grams equals the relative atomic mass of that element. One mole of hydrogen atoms has a mass of 1 gram; one mole of carbon atoms has a mass of 12 grams. One mole consists of 6.022×10^{23} atoms. This figure is called Avogadro's number, named after Italian scientist Amedeo Avogadro (1776–1856).

◀ *Flames are produced when water reacts with sodium metal. During this violent reaction, a sodium atom replaces one of the hydrogen atoms in the water molecule to form sodium hydroxide and hydrogen gas.*

enough heat to get other molecules to react, and the fuel burns readily. Sometimes, gentle warming is enough to get a chemical reaction going.

Speed of reaction

A reaction can happen only if molecules of the reactants come together. Reactions of powdered solids are extremely slow, if they happen at all. Fizzy headache tablets work in this way. Powdered citric acid and baking soda in the tablet start to react only when water is added to make them dissolve. Before the water is added, there is little contact between granules of the citric acid and baking soda. The tablets are stable as long as they are dry.

Reactions of liquids and gases occur more readily because the particles intermingle in random motion. In the case of gases, high pressure speeds the reaction along because the reacting particles have less space in which to move. Particles at high pressure therefore collide more often than particles at low pressure. When the reactants are solutions in liquids, high concentration also increases the speed

of molecules that have enough energy to react, so the reaction goes faster. In fact, reaction rates double for each increase of 18°F (10°C).

Catalysts are materials that speed up reactions without taking part in the reaction themselves. Catalysts typically combine with one or more of the reactants in a way that weakens their bonds. This reduces the height of the hump in the energy curve, so the reaction happens more quickly. After the molecules have reacted, the products drift away from the catalyst so it can trigger another reaction between new reactant molecules.

Which way is forward?

If the products of a reaction collide, there is always the chance that they will react to form the reactants again. This is a waste of time and materials for a chemist who is trying to make a specific product.

Fortunately, there are tricks that can force the reaction in the right direction for the required product. First, chemists prefer to use exothermic reactions that give out a lot of heat (see the diagram below). Second, the chemist may think of a way to

of the reaction. High concentration means there are more reactants present, so there is more chance that the reactant molecules will collide.

The speed of the chemical reaction between a liquid and a solid depends on the particle size of the solid. A lump of chalk (calcium carbonate) reacts with hydrochloric acid much more slowly than the same amount of chalk ground to fine powder. Chalk powder has a much greater surface area than a solid lump of chalk. Therefore, more acid molecules can come into contact with chalk powder. In addition, concentrated hydrochloric acid reacts much more rapidly than dilute acid, because collisions between concentrated acid and the chalk are much more frequent.

Temperature has a great influence on the speed of a reaction. The reactants not only need to collide, but they also need enough energy to get over the energy barrier for the reaction. An increase in temperature dramatically increases the proportion

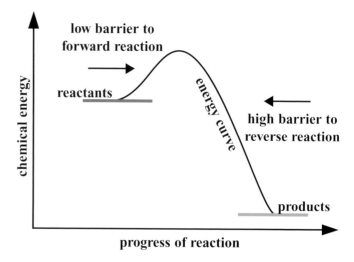

▲ *This diagram shows the energy pathway during an exothermic reaction. The energy barrier for the reverse reaction is much higher than for the forward reaction. The products of the forward reaction are unlikely to reform the reactants during a reverse reaction.*

▶ *Products from drugs and dyes to paint and plastics are produced in bulk at industrial chemical plants. The production of these goods usually requires more than one chemical reaction—the sequence of reactions is called a synthesis (from the Greek for "putting together").*

separate the products from the reaction mixture. If one of the products is a gas, for example, it can be collected as it bubbles out of the liquid reaction mixture, so the reverse reaction cannot happen.

Chemical synthesis

Synthetic chemists use their knowledge of chemical reactions to figure out ways to make new useful products, such as detergents, pesticides, and plastics. There are often several ways to produce the same compound. The choice depends on factors such as availability of materials, ease of reaction, and cost. When producing a test compound, a synthetic chemist will choose the reaction that is easiest to perform in the laboratory.

If a test compound proves useful enough to manufacture in large quantities, a synthetic chemist will choose the reaction that is least wasteful of materials and energy and involves the cheapest reactants. A chemical engineer will then study each step in the overall reaction to spot potential manufacturing problems.

In particular, chemical engineers look for the possibility of a runaway reaction. A runaway reaction may occur if a reaction releases more heat than can escape from the reaction mixture. The temperature rises and, as the mixture gets hotter, the reaction goes faster and releases heat at a faster rate. The end result can be an explosion as the components of the reaction mixture expand and force their way out of the reaction vessel. Runaway reactions can be avoided by keeping concentrations within preset limits and ensuring that the reaction vessel has cooling coils to remove excess heat.

See also: ATOM AND MOLECULE • CATALYST • CHEMISTRY • ENGINEERING

Chemistry

Chemistry is a branch of science that deals with the composition, structure, and properties of different substances. Chemists also study the changes that take place when different substances react. Many chemicals are used to make a range of useful products, from drugs and dyes to paper and plastics. Other chemicals are harmful substances that harm people and the environment.

Anything that has a mass and takes up space is matter. Matter is the air people breathe, the food people eat, and the clothes people wear. Even people themselves are a form of matter. Chemistry is the science that studies matter and the changes that take place with matter. Chemists now know that matter consists of tiny particles called atoms. They also know that atoms are the building blocks of chemical elements. By studying the elements and the compounds formed when elements combine, chemists have gained a greater understanding of the world in which we live.

▲ *This sixteenth-century German woodcut shows two alchemists in a laboratory. Alchemists believed that they could transform common metals such as lead into gold. Although they were incorrect, their studies laid the foundations for modern chemistry.*

The history of chemistry

Modern chemistry is a fairly recent development. Many ancient civilizations knew about metals, such as copper, gold, and iron. They even knew how to mix metals with other substances to make stronger materials, which chemists call alloys. However, most of this knowledge came about by chance. Very little was known about the nature of matter.

Ancient Greek philosophers, such as Aristotle (c. 320–c. 250 BCE), were the first people to think about the composition of substances. They believed that everything on Earth was made from four basic substances: air, earth, fire, and water. Combinations of these four basic elements gave rise to all matter. They also thought that the physical qualities of

different materials, such as color and hardness, could be combined to make materials with the same qualities. In this way, people thought that they could produce precious metals, such as gold, by combining different materials with similar properties to gold. This belief gave rise to the study of alchemy—the precursor to modern chemistry.

For centuries, alchemists spent most of their time searching for an imaginary substance called the philosophers' stone, which they believed was the missing link in the transformation of common metals into gold. Of course, the alchemists never found it, but they did discover many new elements and compounds. In the thirteenth century, some alchemists realized that their search for the philosophers' stone was in vain. Many turned their attention to medicine and tried to make a potion they called the "elixir of life," which would cure diseases and prolong life indefinitely.

At the start of the eighteenth century, people started to use experiments to solve problems and test their theories. One problem that puzzled scientists of the day was combustion—how materials burned. Most people believed that a substance called phlogiston escaped during combustion, but scientists could not prove the existence of phlogiston by experimentation. The answer came in the 1770s. Noting the discovery of a gas (now called oxygen) by English chemist Joseph Priestley (1733–1804), French scientist Antoine-Laurent Lavoisier (1743–1794) proved that materials combine with oxygen when they burn. Lavoisier had described a chemical reaction, and his discovery marked the beginning of modern chemistry.

Modern chemistry

Chemistry advanced very quickly in the nineteenth century. In 1805, English scientist John Dalton (1766–1844) published his theory of the atom, in which he proposed that matter consists of tiny particles called atoms. Dalton suggested that chemical reactions occur between these atoms or groups of atoms. Around the same time, another English chemist, Humphry Davy (1778–1829), added to the ever-growing list of chemical elements. As chemists identified more and more chemical elements, they realized that some were more alike than others. Similar trends in the physical and chemical properties of elements

▼ *This engraving shows Humphry Davy giving a lecture at the Royal Institution in London. During his distinguished career as a chemist, Davy discovered a number of new chemical elements, including calcium, magnesium, potassium, and sodium.*

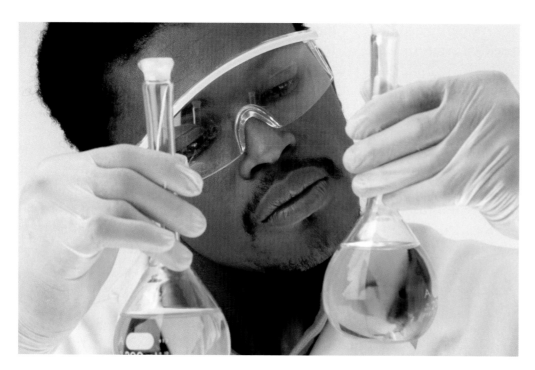

◄ An analytical chemist examines a mixture of different chemicals. Chemical analysis is an important part of modern chemistry. For example, it has been used to identify the harmful by-products of industrial processes and so prevent them from polluting the environment.

enabled Russian chemist Dmitry Mendeleyev (1834–1907) to publish the periodic table of chemical elements and predict the existence of elements that had yet to be discovered.

Twentieth-century chemistry built on these solid foundations and heralded many new discoveries. The work of New Zealand–born British scientist Ernest Rutherford (1871–1937) paved the way for Danish physicist Niels Bohr (1885–1962) and his description of atomic structure. Radioactivity was described by French chemists Antoine-Henri Becquerel (1852–1908) and Marie (1867–1934) and Pierre Curie (1859–1906). Their work led to the discovery of artificial chemical elements, which are still being discovered today.

DID YOU KNOW?

Organometallic chemistry is the study of certain molecules that link a metal atom and a carbon atom. An example is the "lead" in gasoline, which is really tetraethyl lead. Other organometallic compounds are used to make plastics such as polythene. Some important industrial processes depend on organometallic chemistry.

Branches of modern chemistry

Chemistry can now be divided into three main branches. Inorganic chemistry is the study of substances found in nonliving sources, such as minerals. Organic chemistry is the study of compounds that contain carbon, many of which are found in living organisms. Physical chemistry is the study of the physical properties and quantities that control the chemical behavior of substances. These physical aspects include the structure of atoms and molecules and the energy used up or released when chemical reactions take place.

Although chemists usually work in specialized fields, they may study some aspects of all three main branches of chemistry. For example, a biochemist may study any kind of reaction that takes place in a living organism. This study can involve inorganic, organic, and physical chemistry.

Elements and compounds

Everything in the universe consists of tiny particles called atoms. The simplest substances contain just one type of atom, and they are called elements. There are about 90 elements that exist in nature, but they are usually found combined with other elements. Another 23 elements have been made artificially in laboratories.

Combinations of two or more elements are called compounds. Common salt is a compound. Chemists call it sodium chloride because it is a combination of the elements sodium and chlorine. Sodium and chlorine atoms join readily with other kinds of atoms, too, so there are many other sources of sodium and chlorine besides sodium chloride. Some elements, such as gold and copper, combine less easily with other atoms. As a result, these elements can often be found as a pure element in nature, and they are known as native deposits.

For many years, chemists thought that six elements, called the inert or noble gases, did not form compounds with other elements. They now know that three noble gases—xenon, krypton, and radon—do form a few compounds. However, chemists have yet to make compounds with the other three inert gases—helium, neon, and argon.

▲ *An industrial chemist conducts a laboratory reaction to see if it will work on an industrial scale. Industrial chemists monitor all stages of large-scale reactions, from the development of new products to the safe handling of dangerous substances.*

Symbols and formulas

Chemists use symbols to represent the elements and to show how they combine together to form compounds. The same symbols are used throughout the world, so any chemist can understand the work of another, even if they do not speak the same language. Each chemical symbol represents just one atom of an element. The symbol for hydrogen, for example, is H. Usually, two hydrogen atoms join together to form one molecule of hydrogen. This is represented by the formula H_2. Two atoms of hydrogen plus one atom of oxygen combine to make water. Most people will recognize the chemical formula for water: H_2O.

Another example is the compound sodium chloride, which has the chemical formula NaCl. This shows chemists that one molecule of sodium chloride contains one sodium atom (Na) and one chlorine atom (Cl). Some compounds contain the atoms of many different elements. For example, sodium bicarbonate (baking soda) has the formula $NaHCO_3$. One molecule of sodium bicarbonate contains one sodium atom (Na), one hydrogen atom (H), one carbon atom (C), and three oxygen atoms (O). The main use of such symbols and formulas is to show scientists and students alike what happens when chemical reactions take place.

Looking at catalysts

Chemical processes play a vital part in making most of the everyday products people use. Important chemical products include detergents, dyes, explosives, and varnishes. The chemical industry also produces medicines to help combat disease.

Catalysts are important in the chemical industry. They help a reaction between two compounds, but they do not get used up during the reaction. Without the catalyst, the reaction might go so slowly that only very small amounts of the product would result. The product would then be very expensive.

See also: BIOCHEMISTRY • CHEMICAL REACTION • INORGANIC CHEMISTRY • ORGANIC CHEMISTRY • PHYSICAL CHEMISTRY

Chromatography

Chromatography is the method used to separate pure substances from mixtures. Scientists use this technique to find out things such as the amount of pesticides in food or the exact contents of a blood or urine sample.

In 1903, Russian botanist Mikhail Tsvet (1872–1919) decided to separate the pigments (coloring matter) in some plant leaves. He dissolved the pigments in a chemical solvent called ether and poured the solution through a column of crushed limestone in a glass tube. Tsvet then poured more ether into the tube, and the pigments washed slowly downward. Tsvet found that the different pigments traveled down through the tube at different speeds, and the mixture separated into different colored bands—one band for each pigment. The technique of chromatography was born. The word *chromatography* comes from the Greek words *khroma*, meaning "color," and *graphia*, which means "writing."

Paper chromatography

Two main kinds of chromatography—paper chromatography and gas chromatography—are now used to analyze mixtures of different chemicals. In paper chromatography, a piece of

▼ *A chemist uses a liquid chromatograph to analyze blueberry extract for chemicals called flavonoids. Today, computers are often used to interpret the results of chromatographic separations.*

CHROMATOGRAPHY

You will need: different food colorings, four small dishes, eye dropper, blotting paper strips, four small jars, water, binder clips, and pencils.

1. Pour tiny amounts of different food colorings into each of the small dishes to make different mixtures of colors.

2. Use an eye dropper to put a tiny drop of each color mixture on the end of a strip of blotting paper.

3. Pour some water into each small jar. Suspend each blotting paper strip from a clip on a pencil. Make sure the color drop dips into the water. After ten minutes, you will see that the water has carried the inks up through the blotting paper, separating them into the different colors again.

As the water soaks through the blotting paper, the dye molecules in the food colorings also move up the paper. Some dye molecules dissolve in the water better than others, so they are carried farther up the blotting paper. Other dye molecules do not dissolve very well, so they are left near the bottom of the blotting paper. This technique of splitting colors using blotting paper is called paper chromatography. Forensic scientists use this technique to identify ink and dye molecules at crime scenes.

thick filter paper is the separation column. Spots of the test sample are first dotted near one edge of the paper. The paper is then dipped into the solvent. As the solvent travels through the paper, it carries the test sample with it. Different ingredients in the sample are carried different distances, depending on how much they are dissolved by the solvent liquid. The separation may take several hours.

In a more recent method, the paper is replaced by a thin layer of powder, such as alumina or silica, spread evenly over a glass plate. This speeds up the separation process, taking around 20 minutes.

Gas chromatography

Gas chromatography is a highly efficient way of separating mixtures of different substances. First, a sample is injected as a gas into the top of a tube. The tube is then filled with a liquid or solid, and the sample is carried through the liquid or solid by gas under pressure. Substances in the gas sample travel through the tube at different rates. The substances that are slowed down most come out last.

See also: DYE AND DYEING • FORENSIC SCIENCE

325

Circulatory system

The circulatory system consists of a network of vessels through which oxygen, nutrients, waste products, hormones, and disease-fighting cells move around the body. The heart is the center of the circulatory system. It pumps a transport fluid called blood through the vessels to every cell in the body.

A number of organs work together to keep blood flowing around the human body. The heart is a muscular pump that forces blood around the body. Blood flows from the heart through vessels called arteries and returns to the heart through vessels called veins. The lungs put oxygen into the blood, and the liver and the intestines supply the blood with nutrients. The kidneys keep the blood free from poisonous chemicals.

The discovery of circulation

English physician William Harvey (1578–1657) was the first person to describe the circulation of blood around the body. In 1628, his text *De Motu Cordis et Sanguinis in Animalibus* (On the Motion of the Heart and Blood in Animals) put to an end the influence of Greek physician Galen (c. 130–c. 200 BCE), whose incorrect ideas about circulation had persisted for more than 1,400 years.

Galen believed that blood was made from food in the liver. He also suggested that blood flowed away from the heart through veins and flowed back to the heart through the same veins. This so-called "ebb-and-flow" theory of circulation persisted for centuries. Then Harvey came up with a simple experiment to prove Galen wrong.

Harvey tied a tourniquet around the upper part of his arm and watched as the veins in the lower part of his arm became swollen with blood. He then stroked a vein in his lower arm upward with his

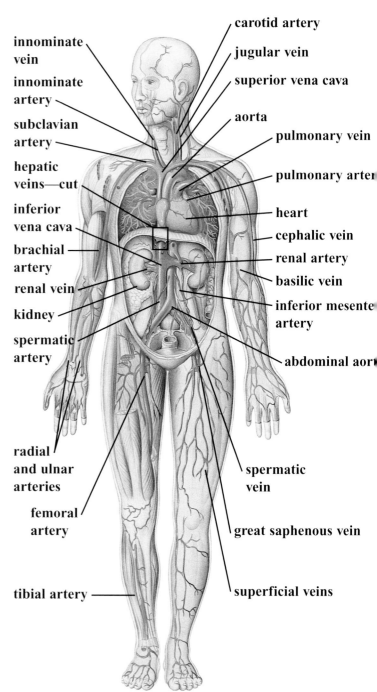

▲ *This illustration shows the main arteries and veins of the male human circulatory system. Blood transports oxygen, hormones, and disease-fighting cells directly to specific organs and tissues. It also carries nutrients and waste products from digested food to and from every cell in the human body. In a female, the spermatic vein and artery are replaced by the ovarian vein and artery.*

Labels: carotid artery, jugular vein, superior vena cava, aorta, pulmonary vein, pulmonary artery, heart, cephalic vein, renal artery, basilic vein, inferior mesenteric artery, abdominal aorta, spermatic vein, great saphenous vein, superficial veins, innominate vein, innominate artery, subclavian artery, hepatic veins—cut, inferior vena cava, brachial artery, renal vein, kidney, spermatic artery, radial and ulnar arteries, femoral artery, tibial artery finger. According to the ebb-and-flow theory, when Harvey removed his finger the blood would have flowed back along the vein toward his wrist. However, Harvey's experiment showed that the vein remained empty between the tourniquet and the point along the vein where he had removed the his finger. Anatomists have since found out that valves in the veins prevent blood from flowing backward, away from the heart.

Harvey performed dissections on mammals, such as dogs, to figure out exactly how the circulatory system works. He showed that blood travels in a loop around the body, moving away from the heart in arteries and back toward the heart in veins. He also showed that blood in mammals is pumped from the right side of the heart to the lungs. The blood then flows to the right side of the heart and is then pumped around the body. Harvey did not have a microscope, but he also predicted

▲ *This portrait of William Harvey was painted after 1628, when Harvey first published his theory of blood circulation. At the time, medicine centered on the ideas of Greek physician Galen.*

▶ *This illustration shows the cycle of blood through the heart, which produces a characteristic sound, often described as "lubb-dubb." First, the ventricles fill with blood (1) and contract. Blood presses against the mitral and tricuspid valves, producing the "lubb" sound (2). Blood leaves the ventricles (3) and, as the ventricles relax, the blood presses back against the semilunar valves. This produces the "dubb" sound (4). The atria then fill up (5), and the cycle repeats.*

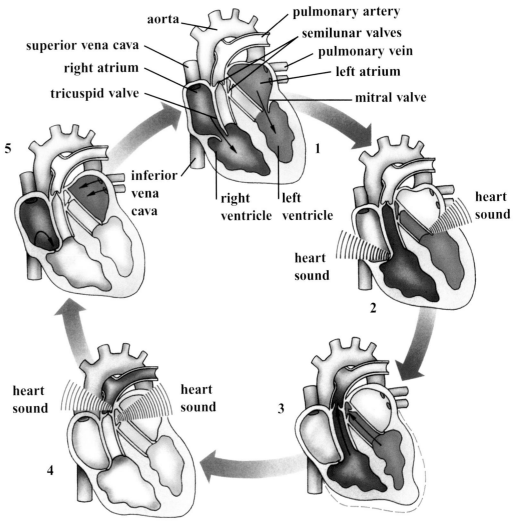

327

that arteries and veins are linked by tiny blood vessels (now called capillaries). In 1661, Italian physician Marcello Malpighi (1628–1694) used an early microscope to look at the fine network of capillaries covering air sacs in the lungs of a frog.

CIRCULATORY COMPONENTS

Harvey's work paved the way for a greater understanding of the human circulatory system. New discoveries have been made as medical technology has improved and as medicine has become more specialized. Physicians now know that the circulatory system consists of many different organs, tissues, and cells. All these circulatory components work together to ensure that blood is kept pumping around the body.

The heart

The heart is a hollow, pear-shaped muscle that lies just left of center in the chest, between the lungs. The heart works by making squeezing motions, called contractions, that pump blood into arteries and transport it around the body. The pumping action can be felt as a beat called the pulse.

There are two sides to the heart, which are divided by a muscular wall called the septum. Each side consists of two chambers. The upper chambers are called atria (*singular,* atrium). The lower chambers are called ventricles.

The left side of the heart pumps blood around the body. The blood first passes into a large artery called the aorta. It is carried to the places it is needed by the many other arteries of the body. As the blood moves around, it delivers oxygen to cells and collects waste carbon dioxide. Through a vein called the vena cava, blood returns to the heart's right side to get rid of the waste material.

The right side pumps blood into the lungs through the pulmonary artery. The lungs replace the lost oxygen in the blood, and the refreshed (oxygenated) blood is returned to the left side through the pulmonary vein.

Both sides of the heart go through all their motions at exactly the same time, so only one heartbeat is felt as the pulse.

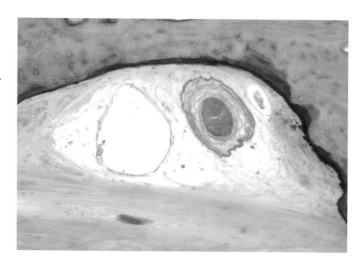

▲ *This picture shows cross sections through an artery (right) and a vein (left). Arteries have thick, elastic, muscular walls. Veins have thin, flexible walls.*

Blood vessels

There are three main types of blood vessels: arteries, veins, and capillaries. Arteries consist of three layers: an inner lining called the tunica interna; a layer of muscle called the tunica media; and a thick layer of elastic tissue called the tunica externa. The strong, elastic, and muscular walls expand and contract as waves of blood are pumped from the heart. As arteries get farther away from the heart, they branch into smaller vessels called arterioles, and then into capillaries.

Capillaries are tiny, narrow blood vessels. The outer wall of a capillary is just one cell thick so the blood in the capillary can supply cells with oxygen and nutrients and remove waste products. Networks of capillaries spread through the tissues of the body and then merge to form venules, which merge to form veins.

Veins consist of three main layers, but each layer is thinner and more flexible than those of arteries. The walls of veins can expand to hold large volumes of blood. Contractions of muscles around the veins help push the blood back toward the heart. Valves prevent blood from moving backward.

Blood

An average man has about 10 pints (5.7 liters) of blood in his body. A woman has slightly less, and a child weighing 100 pounds (45 kilograms) may

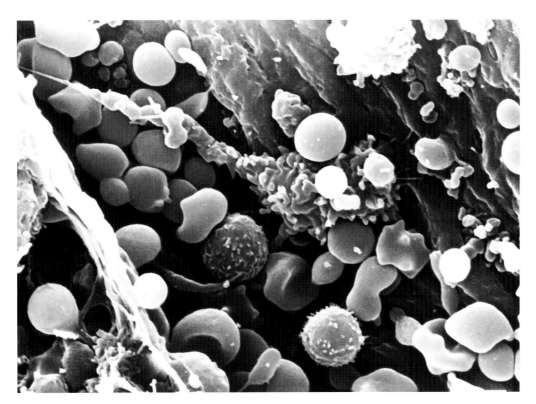

This microscopic image shows red blood cells and white blood cells in the spleen. Red blood cells (shown in red) are broken down in the spleen, and the iron they contain is recycled back into the body. Two types of white blood cells are shown in this picture. Both the lymphocytes (blue) and the granulocyte (green; in the center of the picture) are active parts of the body's immune system, destroying bacteria and other invaders.

have only 6 pints (3.4 liters). Around 45 percent of the blood consists of red blood cells, white blood cells, and cell fragments called platelets, each designed for a special task. These blood cells and cell fragments float in a pale yellow liquid called plasma, made up mostly of water.

Red blood cells are doughnut-shaped cells measuring just a tiny fraction of an inch across. There are about as many as five million red blood cells in every drop of blood. These cells get their red color from an iron-containing substance called hemoglobin. The hemoglobin in the cells picks up oxygen from the air that is breathed into the lungs. The oxygen in the red blood cells is then carried all over the body. When the red cells give up the oxygen, they change from a bright red to a dark red or purple color. As the cells change, the hemoglobin picks up waste carbon dioxide. The red blood cells then carry the carbon dioxide back to the lungs, where it is breathed out.

White blood cells are slightly bigger than red blood cells. One drop of blood contains between 8,000 and 10,000 white blood cells. White blood cells are part of the body's immune system. They destroy microorganisms and other particles in the blood to prevent infection. White cells can even break down large objects such as thorns and wood splinters. There are two main kinds of white blood cells: granulocytes and lymphocytes. Granulocytes attack foreign objects by engulfing them. If a cut is infected by bacteria, for example, granulocytes rush to the wound and surround and then engulf the bacteria. They act very quickly to stop an infection from spreading. Lymphocytes act more slowly. They seem to use the blood as a means of transport from one part of the body to another. Unlike red blood cells, white cells can pass out of the blood vessels and into other body tissues.

There are about 15 million platelets in every drop of blood. Platelets are small blood cell fragments—much smaller than red blood cells. They are involved in the blood-clotting process. People can lose up to one-seventh of the total volume of their blood without any ill effects, but a greater loss can be very serious. Blood clotting prevents too much blood from escaping. When a blood vessel is damaged, platelets gather around and stick to the site of the injury, and to each other, forming a kind of plug that seals off the damaged vessel. The plug stays in place until the body has repaired the damaged vessel.

CIRCULATORY PROBLEMS

Many different diseases affect the circulatory system. Genetics plays a part in the incidence of many blood and heart disorders. In other cases, lifestyle choices, such as physical inactivity, poor eating habits, and smoking tobacco, increase the chance of people developing circulatory disorders. One of the main objectives of modern medicine is to make people aware of the risks associated with unhealthy lifestyle choices.

Heart diseases

Heart attacks occur when a blood clot blocks one of the arteries leading away from the heart. The medical term for a heart attack is *coronary thrombosis*. A heart attack may result in instant death, or it may damage the heart muscle so badly that it makes a person an invalid. In other cases, the

▼ *A physician uses an electrocardiogram (ECG) to perform a heart stress test, which measures the output of the patient's heart during exercise. Physicians use heart stress tests to assess the health of the heart and measure the patient's risk of having a heart attack.*

DID YOU KNOW?

If a patient needs a blood transfusion, the physician must first find out which blood group that person has. There are several different groups of human blood. The blood of most people is one of the four main groups: A, B, AB, or O. Blood from some groups cannot safely be given to people with other blood groups. If the wrong blood is given to the patient, the patient's blood plasma will attack the donor's red blood cells and destroy them.

heart attack is so mild that a person will recover almost completely. Deposits called plaques can form inside blood vessels, making them narrower. The blood can clot, or thicken, around the plaques, which can stop the flow of blood. If this happens in an artery leading to the heart, then the result is a heart attack. If the blocked vessel leads to the brain, the result is known as a stroke.

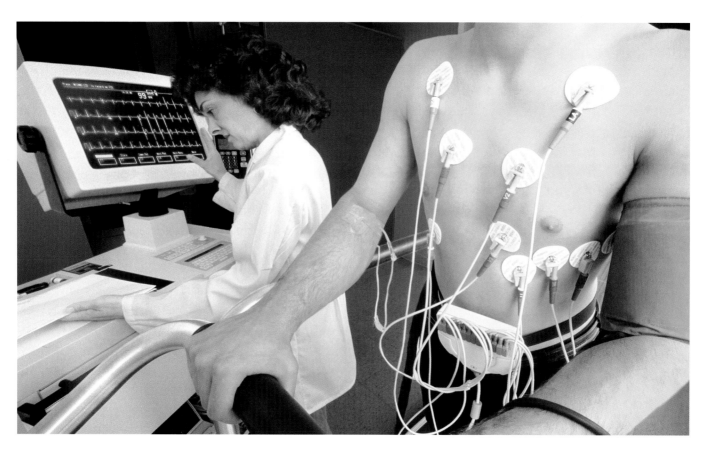

▶ *Cigarette smoking is a very unhealthy habit. As well as being one of the main causes of heart disease, smoking may lead to stroke, lung disease, and several types of cancer.*

People with heart diseases now live much longer thanks to new medical treatments. New drugs have been discovered, and new operations to repair damaged hearts or transplant new ones have also been developed. New drugs dissolve blood clots. If the drugs are given soon after a stroke or heart attack, they can restore blood flow before the oxygen-starved cells become too badly damaged. Heart transplants are now routine. One reason is that a new drug called cyclosporin stops the body's immune system from rejecting the new heart.

Blood diseases

Hematology is concerned with diseases of the blood. Some blood diseases, such as leukemia and sickle-cell anemia, develop in childhood or later life. AIDS has emerged as a serious blood disease.

Some people are born with the blood disease sickle-cell anemia. Up to a quarter of all people of African or Afro-Caribbean origin carry one copy of the sickle-cell gene. They may be perfectly healthy, but someone with two copies of the gene will suffer from sickle-cell anemia. If two carriers have a child together, there is one chance in four that the child will have the disease. The child may die as a result.

One job for hematologists is to talk to couples who are at risk of having babies with sickle-cell anemia. If they do have a baby, they will be offered a diagnosis early in the pregnancy. Physicians test for sickle-cell anemia by taking a DNA sample of the membranes produced by the fetus in the mother's uterus. If the test proves positive, the couple may be offered genetic counseling before they decide to have the baby.

See also: AIDS • BRAIN • CELL • DIGESTIVE SYSTEM • DISEASE • GENETICS • IMMUNE SYSTEM • MEDICAL TECHNOLOGY • RESPIRATORY SYSTEM

Classification

Biologists need to organize the natural world to reflect the way in which living things have evolved. Classification is the science of organizing different life-forms. Through classification, biologists can understand how and where an organism fits on the tree of life.

Scientists arrange different organisms into categories that reflect their phylogeny, or line of descent from a common ancestor. This process is called classification. Classification helps organize and communicate information about the living world. It can show relationships between different groups and indicates the evolutionary history of different organisms. Classification is based on features such as structure, development, and body chemistry. Recently, genetic analysis has also proved to be an important tool in classification.

The history of classification

Greek thinker Aristotle (384–322 BCE) was the first person to develop a system for classifying the natural world. Aristotle dissected and studied hundreds of animals and classified them according to how they moved. His system, published in a book entitled *Historia Animalium* ("The History of Animals"), remained in use for more than two thousand years. Aristotle's system was replaced by a new type of classification in the middle of the eighteenth century. This system was pioneered by Swedish botanist Carolus Linnaeus (1707–1778). Linnaeus divided all organisms into one of two main groups—the animal kingdom or the plant kingdom. Then he divided each kingdom into smaller and smaller categories, eventually ending up with species to describe individual organisms.

Linnaeus came up with a system, called the binomial system, for naming different organisms. For example, he placed the European starling in a group, or genus, called *Sturnus,* along with other starlings. To signify the European starling alone, he added the Latin name *vulgaris,* which means "common," to the genus name. So, the full name of the European starling according to Linnaeus's binomial system is *Sturnus vulgaris.*

The tree of life

Biologists still use the binomial system, together with the Latin that was the language of science in Linnaeus's time. Later, biologists expanded and modified Linnaeus's system, after English naturalist Charles Darwin (1809–1882) suggested that all creatures on Earth were related and could be traced back to a common ancestor. New levels of classification were added to Linnaeus's binomial system, such as phylum, class, order, and family.

Dog breeds come in many different shapes and sizes. However, they are all classified as the same species: **Canis familiaris.** *Each breed is the product of a deliberate process of artificial selection by people over the last 100,000 years.*

The class Mammalia is divided into many orders. One of these orders is the Carnivora, or carnivores, which includes gray wolves. The next series of branches include families such as the Canidae, which includes just the dogs and their relatives. Several species of dogs are grouped into the genus *Canis,* while the final twig on this branch of our tree denotes the gray wolf, *Canis lupus.*

▲ *Swedish botanist Carolus Linnaeus, who introduced the binomial system of classification in his celebrated work* **Species Plantarum,** *published in 1753.*

Perhaps the best way to think of the classification system is to imagine life on Earth as parts of a huge tree. Branches from the tree trunk represent different groups, with each fork in the branch representing a new subdivision. Large branches divide into smaller branches, until eventually the smallest twigs represent individual species. A modern classification shows exactly where on this tree of life a group of organisms sits.

The gray wolf is a distinct species on this tree of life. Like all animals, gray wolves belong to the kingdom Animalia. The kingdom is one of the largest branches, stemming directly from the tree trunk. The next branch of gray wolf classification, the phylum Chordata, includes all animals with stiff rods, called notochords, running along their bodies. A subdivision of the Chordata, the Vertebrata, forms a group called a subphylum that includes all vertebrates (animals with backbones). Next comes the class Mammalia, or mammals, which also includes humans.

DID YOU KNOW?

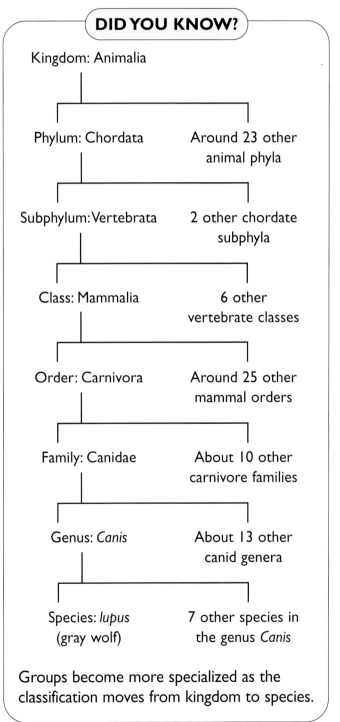

Kingdom: Animalia

Phylum: Chordata — Around 23 other animal phyla

Subphylum: Vertebrata — 2 other chordate subphyla

Class: Mammalia — 6 other vertebrate classes

Order: Carnivora — Around 25 other mammal orders

Family: Canidae — About 10 other carnivore families

Genus: *Canis* — About 13 other canid genera

Species: *lupus* (gray wolf) — 7 other species in the genus *Canis*

Groups become more specialized as the classification moves from kingdom to species.

Understanding subspecies

Sometimes, naming a species alone is not enough to provide a full classification. Many species are divided again into subspecies, depending on variables such as geographical range. To account for this, biologists add a third name to the species. So, if the gray wolf in the previous example was the North American subspecies, its full name would be *Canis lupus occidentalis*. If the gray wolf came from Europe, its name would be *Canis lupus lupus*.

Modern methods

Biologists use several different methods to see if organisms are related to one another. Studies of deoxyribonucleic acid (DNA)—the molecule that forms genes—provide important clues about how closely related different creatures are. The more similarities there are between the genetic code of two organisms, the more closely the two organisms are related. DNA research has recently shown that American vultures, such as condors, are only distantly related to African and Asian vultures, even though they look very similar. American vultures are in fact more closely related to storks. By estimating the rate of change of DNA over time, biologists can also figure out how long ago different species diverged from a common ancestor.

Clockwise from bottom left: a chipmunk, a fruit bat, a kangaroo and its joey, a killer whale, and an African elephant. There are about 5,000 species of living mammals (class Mammalia). All of them have body hair and nourish their young with milk produced by female mammary glands.

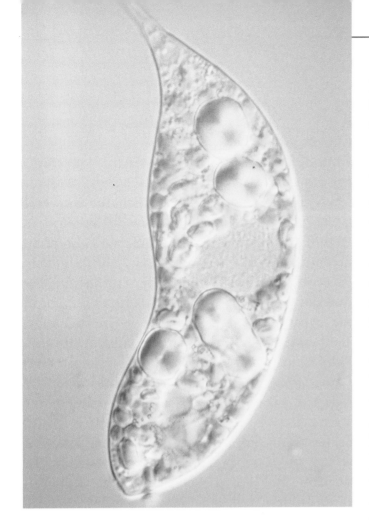

▲ **Euglena** *is a single-celled organism that has both plant- and animal-like characteristics. Like plants,* **Euglena** *makes food by photosynthesis. It also has a whiplike flagellum, a characteristic of the animal kingdom, that enables it to move.* **Euglena** *was once classified as a plant. It is now in the kingdom Protista and regarded as distinct from both plants and animals.*

The importance of cladistics

DNA can only very rarely be extracted from fossils. Biologists use a different technique, called cladistics, to produce a reliable phylogenetic tree that includes fossil ancestors. Cladistics involves looking at anatomical features and figuring out which ones are present in a group but absent in a distant ancestor. These features are called shared derived characteristics. For example, wombats and groundhogs look very similar and have similar lifestyles. However, wombats raise their young in a pouch on the body, while young groundhogs grow inside the female's body—in the same way as humans. Both humans and groundhogs are nourished by a placenta as they develop. The placenta is a shared derived characteristic of groundhogs and humans, which suggests these two species are more closely related to each other than either is to the wombat.

Cladistics is important because it allows biologists to trace the evolution of groups of organisms as their features change over time. For example, biologists once assumed that spiders that weave complex and intricate fly-catching orb-webs evolved from spiders that produced messy tangles of cobwebs. Cladistics has shown that the truth is in fact the reverse—cobweb-spinning spiders evolved from orb-web weavers.

Changing kingdoms

The classification of the living world is constantly under revision due to new scientific developments, such as the discovery of new species. Even the very highest taxonomic groupings—the kingdoms—have frequently been reviewed and altered by taxonomists. When Linnaeus came up with his classification system, he separated the natural world into two kingdoms. By the 1970s, genetic research had broadened the number of kingdoms to six—animals, plants, fungi, protists (single-celled organisms such as amoebas), and two types of bacteria (the archaebacteria and eubacteria).

However, recent DNA analysis has shown that this classification is misleading. Taxonomists now suggest that life should be divided into three vast "domains." Two, called the bacteria and archaea, consist of single-celled organisms that do not have cell nuclei. The third domain, called the eukaryota, consists of organisms made up of cells that do have nuclei. Animals and many other groups belong to the eukaryota. There are many divisions within these domains that run at least as deep as the separation between animals and plants. There are now thought to be at least 12 eukaryote kingdoms, and there may be more than 30 kingdoms in total.

See also: ANIMAL KINGDOM • BACTERIA • FUNGI KINGDOM • PLANT KINGDOM • PROTIST KINGDOM • VIRUS, BIOLOGICAL

Climate

In the course of a single day, one place may be sunny, warm, dry, wet, and windy. Yet it is the combination of all these weather elements, and more, that makes up the climate of a particular location. Climate is important for many reasons. It influences landscape, plants, and wildlife. It governs what crops can be grown, what types of homes people build, and what clothes they wear.

Many factors influence the climate of an area. These include its distance from the equator, its altitude (height above sea level), its distance from the ocean, its exposure to the prevailing wind, and even the local vegetation. Taken together, these factors all the features of the area's climate.

▼ *Mountains have different climate zones because the air temperature decreases with increasing altitude. In turn, the climate influences the vegetation that grows on the mountain. Lower slopes are often dominated by conifer forests. High mountaintops are covered by a permanent layer of snow and ice.*

Climate and latitude

Latitude is one of the main factors governing climate. At any location between 23 degrees latitude south and 23 degrees latitude north, the Sun's rays strike Earth's surface on some day during the year. Within these latitudes, seasonal changes also occur because Earth is tilted on its axis. Thus, different parts of Earth are closer to the Sun at different times of the year. It is in the band on either side of the equator that the Sun is at its most intense. Temperatures are very warm throughout the year. Farther north and south, the Sun's rays must travel farther through the atmosphere. More sunlight is reflected back out to space by particles in the atmosphere. So it is generally coolest in places farthest away from the equator. During the arctic winter, for example, the Sun barely rises above the horizon for several weeks, and the region is shrouded in darkness.

Climate and altitude

At high altitude, such as on a mountaintop, the atmosphere contains fewer particles than the atmosphere at sea level. The air in high places is less able to absorb the Sun's heat. Air temperature cools with height at a rate of 3.5°F per 1,000 feet (6.4°C

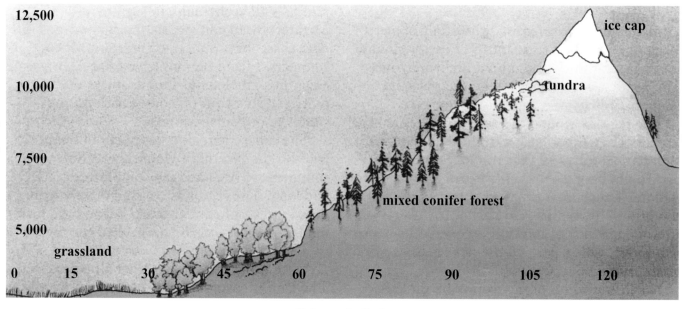

distance (miles)

per 1,000 meters). There is snow on the summit of Mount Kilimanjaro in Tanzania. The mountain lies just below the equator, but it is 19,340 feet (5,895 meters) above sea level.

If moist air meets an area of high altitude, it rises and cools. The water vapor in the air condenses (turns to liquid) and falls as rain or snow. Therefore, mountain ranges close to coastal regions with onshore prevailing winds experience higher levels of precipitation than their low-lying equivalents.

Ocean's influence

Earth's oceans influence the climate of a region because they heat and cool more slowly than the surface of the land. The closer a place is to a large body of water, the cooler the temperature during the warmest months of the year and the milder the temperature during the colder months. The opposite applies to places far from an ocean. The influence of ocean temperature is sometimes reinforced by warm ocean currents such as the Gulf Stream. Land areas close to oceans may experience increased precipitation if the prevailing wind direction is from the sea. If the wind generally blows from the land over the sea, precipitation is generally lower.

Wind patterns

Circulatory patterns within the atmosphere constantly redistribute heat around Earth's surface. Wind patterns also affect the climate of an area. For example, the northeast trade winds are vigorous winds that blow from areas of high pressure in midlatitudes in the Northern Hemisphere. The roaring forties are strong north-westerly winds—often gales—that blow from midlatitude high-pressure areas in the Southern Hemisphere. Both are important elements of the climate of large parts of Earth's surface.

Koeppen classification

Many other factors help produce the unique climate of an area. These include geology, soil type, vegetation, and urban development, among others. For more than two centuries, however, people have

▲ *Two children collect water during a drought in India. A drought occurs when a region experiences much less rainfall than usual. Many climate experts link the worldwide increase in droughts to global warming.*

DID YOU KNOW?

Some areas of Earth have truly inhospitable climates. Oimyakon in Siberia is one of the coldest places in the world. In January, the mean temperature is –60°F (–51°C). Daytime temperatures rarely exceed 50°F (10°C) in the warmest month of the year. Cherrapunji in India also has an extreme climate but for a very different reason. Cherrapunji lies at an altitude of 4,300 feet (1,313 meters). This hilly position encourages heavy rainfall from the summer monsoon. In June, rainfall averages more than 8 feet (2.5 meters), while the annual figure is almost 36 feet (11 meters). By contrast, Aswan in Egypt has a true desert climate. It averages just more than 1/10 inch (3 millimeters) of rain each year. The climate is made harsher by mean summer temperatures of more than 86°F (30°C).

tried to group areas with similar climates. The two weather elements relied upon most heavily in describing different climates are temperature and precipitation. Most modern climate classifications are based on a system devised by German scientist Wladimir Koeppen (1846–1940) in 1918. He described five main climate zones: tropical rainy, dry, warm midlatitude (warm temperate), cool midlatitude (cool temperate), and polar.

Tropical rainy climates have a mean temperature of at least 64°F (18°C) every month. They are further subdivided into monsoon, wet and dry, and wet all year. Tropical rainy climates are most common in the world's rain forests, such as those in the Amazon basin. Dry climates are characterized by a low annual precipitation. Koeppen proposed two main subdivisions: semiarid steppe climate and arid desert. Dry climates occur both in tropical and midlatitude regions. Warm midlatitude climates have a mean temperature in the coldest month between 27°F (–3°C) and 64°F (18°C) and a mean temperature in at least one month of 50°F (10°C)

or more. This zone is subdivided according to whether it has a dry summer (Mediterranean climate), a dry winter, or no dry season. Cool midlatitude climates have a mean temperature of less than 27°F (–3°C) in the coldest month and a mean temperature of more than 50°F (10°C) in the warmest month. Again, this can be subdivided. Polar climates are characterized by a mean temperature below 50°F (10°C) every month. They are further split into areas where the mean temperature in the warmest month is above 32°F (0°C), such as in the Tibetan Plateau and much of the high Andes, or where the temperature is below freezing, such as interior Greenland and Antarctica.

CLIMATE CHANGE

Scientists have found evidence of climate change from many sources. These sources range from historical records and changes in the distribution of animals and plants, to the movements of glaciers

▼ *A map of the world's major climate zones.*

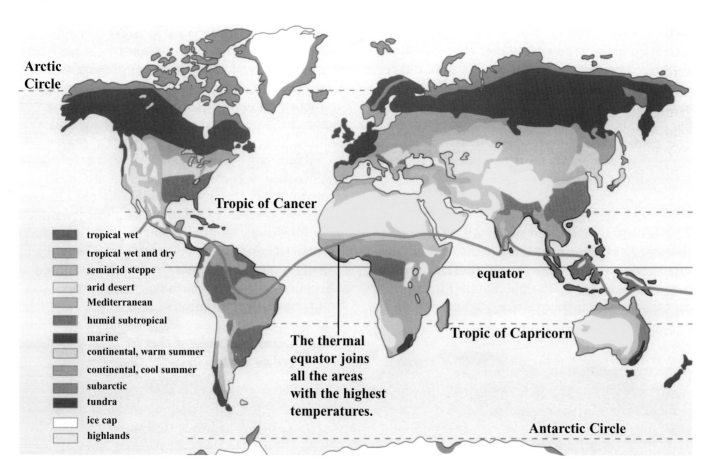

Arctic Circle

Tropic of Cancer

equator

tropical wet
tropical wet and dry
semiarid steppe
arid desert
Mediterranean
humid subtropical
marine
continental, warm summer
continental, cool summer
subarctic
tundra
ice cap
highlands

The thermal equator joins all the areas with the highest temperatures.

Tropic of Capricorn

Antarctic Circle

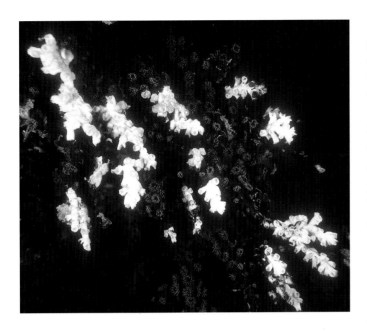

◄ Coral is particularly vulnerable to the effects of global warming. If the ocean temperature rises, the coral spits out tiny algae, called zooxanthellae, and loses its color. This process is known as coral bleaching, and it can damage and even kill entire reef systems.

and the annual growth rings of trees. Past climate changes have been slow and driven by variables that people could not control. However, human activities have made a huge impact on the environment in the past one hundred years. These activities include increased industrialization of the developed world and the widespread use of fossil fuels—coal, petroleum, and natural gas.

Acid rain

Acid rain affects large areas of North America. It damages natural vegetation, crops, and fish stocks. Acid rain is produced when sulfur dioxide gas (SO_2) and nitrous oxides (various chemicals containing nitrogen and oxygen) are pumped into the atmosphere. Some of these chemicals are produced naturally. In the United States, however, around 50 percent of the sulfur dioxide and 25 percent of the nitrous oxides in the atmosphere come from power plants that burn fossil fuels. Sulfur dioxide and nitrous oxides react with water, oxygen, and other chemicals in the atmosphere to form mild, but potentially damaging, sulfuric acid (H_2SO_4) and nitric acid (HNO_3).

Smog

Smog is another type of pollution that has changed the climate in parts of North America and other industrialized nations. In strong sunlight, the nitrous oxides emitted by automobiles and factory chimneys react with other chemicals in the lower atmosphere. These reactions, called photochemical reactions, result in the production of ozone (O_3). A brownish haze forms in the air, which reduces visibility, and many people suffer from headaches, eye irritation, and breathing difficulties.

Global warming

Perhaps the most damaging climate changes have been caused by increases in the temperature of Earth's atmosphere and the oceans—an effect called global warming. While there is much debate about how quickly and by how much the temperatures will rise, most scientists agree that the effects already witnessed are a result of human activities during the last century. When carbon dioxide (CO_2), methane (CH_4), and nitrous oxides—the so-called greenhouse gases—get into the atmosphere, these gases help trap heat from the Sun's rays in the same way as the glass of a greenhouse traps warm air inside. Sunlight passes through the atmosphere and warms Earth, but the greenhouse gases absorb some of the infrared radiation emitted by Earth and reradiate it within the atmosphere. The use of fossil fuels accounts for 98 percent of carbon dioxide emissions, 24 percent of methane emissions, and 18 percent of nitrous oxide emissions in the United States. The National Academy of Science estimates that global temperatures have warmed 1°F (0.6°C) over the course of the twentieth century. The sea level has also risen by 4 to 8 inches (10 to 20 centimeters). Both these increases have accelerated since 1980. It appears that the trend will continue, and the global climatic repercussions could be disastrous.

See also: ATMOSPHERE • GLOBAL WARMING • POLLUTION • WEATHER SYSTEM

Cloning

In nature, clones occur when an organism reproduces asexually (without a partner), or a fertilized egg splits to produce identical offspring. A clone is an exact genetic copy of another organism. Scientists can modify the genetic makeup of plants by genetic engineering and alter microorganisms using biotechnology for medical uses. It is also possible to clone animals, but this is more difficult and controversial.

In 1996, geneticists in the United States cloned two rhesus monkeys using embryo cells. The following year Dolly the sheep was born at the Roslin Institute in Edinburgh, Scotland. Remarkably, Dolly was created from adult cell material taken from the udder of a sheep. These clones are mammals—the biological group to which humans belong. The creation of cloned mammals has raised many ethical questions. In theory, scientists now have the knowledge to clone humans. It should soon be possible for biologists to make exact copies of people.

Natural clones

There are many single-celled organisms, such as yeasts (a type of fungus), that reproduce asexually; that is, without the union of male and female sex cells, or gametes. Many organisms do this by simple cell division. Others produce offspring by budding, or regeneration, of a part of themselves. Some insects, such as aphids, and even some reptiles, such as some python species, reproduce by parthenogenesis. This is a form of reproduction in which eggs develop without being fertilized.

Among vertebrates (animals with a backbone), clones are produced following sexual reproduction if a fertilized egg splits and the resulting bundles of cells develop into offspring. In this case, the offspring are clones of each other, rather than of the parent, as with asexual reproduction. The armadillo is unique, as the embryo divides into four, producing identical quadruplets.

▶ *Identical twins are natural clones, formed when a fertilized egg divides into two as it develops.*

Among plants, asexual reproduction is widespread. In fact, gardeners make use of this ability in plants when they take cuttings for propagation (breeding). Plants that produce long reproductive shoots, or runners (such as the strawberry), underground stems (such as thistles), or spores (such as fungi and ferns) produce daughter plants that are genetically identical to the plant from which they sprouted. Some plants are even capable of reproducing by apomixis, a process in which seeds are produced without fertilization. The Kentucky bluegrasses that grow in lawns across the United States reproduce in this way.

One advantage of a clone is that it preserves the genotype (unique genetic information) of the parent organism, unless a genetic error called a mutation occurs between the generations. Although sexual reproduction has the advantage of providing variation in a population, it does mean

DID YOU KNOW?

The idea of cloning was first put forward in 1938 by German embryologist Hans Spemann (1869–1941). He suggested removing the nucleus of a cell from an embryo, juvenile, or adult and putting it into an enucleated egg (an egg with the nucleus taken out). At that time, however, the technological advances needed to carry out his experiment were not yet available.

there is a good chance that offspring might not inherit every positive characteristic of their parents, because there is genetic mixing during gamete production. Breeding can be all important, particularly to farmers and horticulturalists who want to preserve the purity of a line or type to ensure, for example, high milk and crop yields.

Types of cloning

Much of the cloning that is discussed in the media is reproductive cloning, which is the production of whole individuals from a single cell. There are other

▲ U.S. National Arboretum researchers devised a technique to develop a whole rose plant from a few genetically engineered cells. Genetic engineering is used extensively in horticulture.

types of cloning. DNA (deoxyribonucleic acid) or tissue cloning replicates only very small parts of an individual organism and so is not as controversial as reproductive cloning. On the other hand, therapeutic cloning is a very sensitive issue because the research makes use of human embryo cells. DNA cloning, which is an important part of genetic engineering and biotechnology, has been carried out in laboratories since the 1970s. It involves transferring a fragment of DNA to another organism (usually a bacterium) and incorporating it with plasmid DNA. Plasmid DNA is DNA outside the cell's chromosomes (the parts of the cell containing hereditary information) that is capable of replication. As the organism multiplies, so too does the plasmid DNA, thereby providing a virtually unlimited source of the material being cloned. In this way, scientists can study a particular

HOW DOLLY WAS CLONED

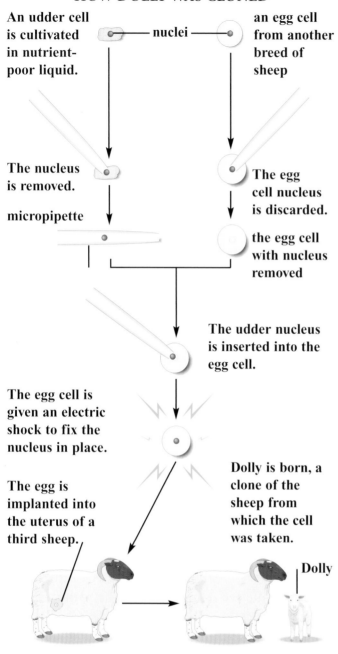

An udder cell is cultivated in nutrient-poor liquid.

nuclei

an egg cell from another breed of sheep

The nucleus is removed.

micropipette

The egg cell nucleus is discarded.

the egg cell with nucleus removed

The udder nucleus is inserted into the egg cell.

The egg cell is given an electric shock to fix the nucleus in place.

Dolly is born, a clone of the sheep from which the cell was taken.

The egg is implanted into the uterus of a third sheep.

Dolly

▲ *Dolly the sheep was the first successful clone of a mammal made using cells specific to a certain purpose (in this case, mammary cells). Dolly proved that it was possible to create a clone without using embryo cells.*

gene of interest or produce certain pharmaceutical products, such as vaccines and antibiotics in volume. Another process, referred to as polymerase chain reactions (PCR), allows scientists to amplify the quantities of DNA obtained from ancient blood, hair, or tissue samples by using enzymes. Genetic engineering is also used in various ways to increase crop yields. For example, the Colorado beetle is responsible for considerable losses from potato crops. However, there is now a genetically engineered potato that produces a toxin to kill the beetle but is harmless to other organisms.

The first experiments in reproductive cloning were carried out on northern leopard frogs in the early 1950s by U.S. scientists Robert Briggs (1911–1983) and Tom King (1921–2000). They separated the cells of an embryo and inserted the nuclei into other enucleated eggs (eggs from which the nuclei had been removed). Twenty-seven eggs hatched into tadpoles, but none survived to adulthood. In 1970, English biologist John Gurdon (1933–) repeated the earlier procedure and again succeeded in producing viable eggs that developed as far as the tadpole stage. Gurdon successfully replaced the nucleus from a frog egg with that of an intestinal cell from a different adult frog. He proved that the process of specialization within cells (which makes them function as bone cells, muscle cells, liver cells, and the like) can be reversed.

For many years, cloning of large animals had little success. Then, in the mid-1980s, cow embryo cells were successfully cloned, and other animals quickly followed. These early successes in cloning were the result of using undifferentiated (non-specialized) embryonic cell nuclei. Using these nuclei, cells retain the ability to develop into all the cell types that a body requires. Dolly, the Dorset Finn sheep clone born in February 1997, was different. She was created from a specialized adult mammary cell. English scientist Ian Wilmut (1944–) managed to reactivate the genes by withholding nourishment from the cultured udder cells before inserting them in the enucleated egg cells. For some reason, this lack of nourishment caused the genes to revert to their undifferentiated embryonic state. Of the 277 attempts using this technique, only Dolly survived. However, Dolly's premature death due to a progressive lung disease raised questions about the cloning procedure.

Other animals have followed, including Cc, a tortoiseshell kitten produced in 2002 by scientists in Texas using a cell from an adult cat; and most recently in 2003, Idaho Gem, a mule clone. This in itself is strange, as mules are the hybrid offspring of a male donkey and a female horse, and most are themselves sterile.

Conservation efforts

Having the ability to produce animals in such ways is thought to have important implications for conservation of endangered species. Noah was a cloned gaur, which is an endangered species of Asian cattle. Only about 36,000 gaur are thought to remain. Noah was produced from genetic material taken from skin cells of a male gaur that died some years previously. The genetic material was injected into enucleated cow egg cells. Of the 692 treated eggs, only Noah was born, and sadly he died of an infection after only 24 hours. The drawback for this kind of work is that females cannot usually carry and give birth to animals of a different species unless they are very closely related, as with the gaur and domestic cattle.

Humans and cloning

The most controversial aspect of producing mammal clones, which has resulted in much heated debate, is whether or not human cloning should be allowed. There is no doubt that in theory it is now possible to clone a human life. Indeed, a number of fertility specialists have already put forward plans to do just that. However, the reality is that the current failure rate in cloning mammals is very

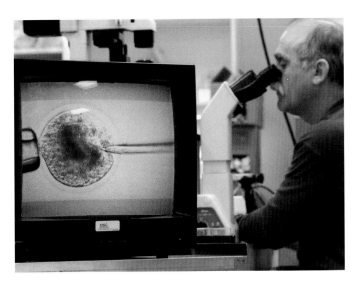

> **DID YOU KNOW?**
>
> Therapeutic cloning may help in the treatment of certain illnesses such as Alzheimer's disease. A viable embryo created from the DNA of a sick person could provide stem cells that would then be used to treat the patient without any risk of rejection.

high (98 percent), and of the remaining 2 percent of clones that are successful, many have health problems or genetic abnormalities.

Therapeutic cloning, also called embryo cloning, is an extremely sensitive field of research because it involves the production of human embryos for research, or the utilization of aborted fetal material. Scientists are interested in the stem cells, which are unspecialized in embryos but also capable of multiplying. Embryonic stem cells were first isolated in 1998 by James Thomson (1958–) of the University of Wisconsin and John Gearhart (1944–) and his colleagues at Johns Hopkins University. Since then, legislation has prohibited progress in this field, except in countries such as Singapore and China.

Looking to the future

The ethical issues of human cloning will take time to resolve. Many people are campaigning both for and against future research on stem cells. There is little doubt they offer a possible solution to people with spinal injuries, such as Christopher Reeve—the U.S. actor famous for his role as Superman. It seems the future of humanity may not after all depend on exploring space but is closer to home—the DNA within us all.

◀ *A pipette is being used to inject modified plasmid DNA cells into a goat egg. As the organism develops, so too does the plasmid DNA. Such DNA cloning is used to rapidly replicate specific genes of use or interest.*

See also: GENETIC ENGINEERING • GENETICS

Cloud

A cloud is a mass of water droplets or ice crystals. These tiny particles are so small they can float in the air. If they grow too big or heavy, they fall to the ground as rain or snow. Clouds come in all shapes and sizes. They play a vital role in the weather patterns on Earth and in the water cycle.

Most clouds are found high in the sky, but the water from which they are made comes from Earth's surface. Heat from the Sun turns liquid water on Earth into an invisible gas called water vapor. This process is called evaporation. Water vapor is carried up into the sky by wind and air currents. This rising water vapor is the starting point for the formation of clouds.

Warm air can carry more water vapor than cold air, so over tropical regions the air often contains more water vapor than over temperate regions. When the air holds as much water vapor as it can carry, it is said to be saturated. Its temperature at this point is its dew point. Since cool air holds less water vapor than warm air, it has a lower dew point.

▼ *Left to right: four cloud formations. Cumulonimbus are storm clouds. Cumulus clouds resembles balls of cotton. Cirrus clouds consist of ice crystals. Altocumulus clouds span the sky in broken groups.*

As warm air rises, it cools. The higher it rises, the cooler it gets. When saturated air rises, some of the water vapor turns into water droplets. This process is called condensation. Clouds form when condensation turns water vapor into water particles. Water droplets usually form around specks of dust in the air. The level in the air where cool air turns water vapor into water droplets is called the condensation level. This level will be higher or lower, depending on the air temperature.

Warm air rises and cools in many ways. For example, warm, moist air may be forced to rise over a mountain. As it rises, it meets cold air higher up and condenses to form orographic clouds. Thunder clouds form when warm air rapidly rises and meets a layer of cold air above. A mass of thunder clouds can reach 60,000 feet (18,000 meters) in height. Other clouds are made when a mass of warm air moves sideways and rises over a mass of cold air. The zone of contact between the warm and cold air is called a warm front. If a mass of cold air moves under a mass of warm air it is called a cold front.

Most clouds consist of liquid water droplets, but some consist of ice crystals. Others contain supercooled water droplets. These droplets do not turn into ice crystals even when the temperature is well below the freezing point of water (32°F; 0°C). Supercooled water freezes only when it touches an ice crystal. Scientists do not know why supercooled water remains liquid at such low temperatures.

Precipitation

Moisture lost from clouds is called precipitation. Rain, snow, sleet, hail, fog, mist, and frost are all forms of precipitation. Rain falls when small droplets of water collide and join to make bigger water droplets. When the water droplets are too heavy to float in the air, they fall as rain. Ice crystals also stick to each other and fall from clouds. If the air below is warm, they will melt and form rain. If it is cold, the crystals fall as snow. Sleet is a mixture of rain and snow, hail is lumps of ice, and fog and mist are clouds of water droplets near the ground.

Trapping heat

As well as being a source of precipitation, clouds also affect the temperatures of the places beneath them. Clouds block incoming sunlight during the day, keeping the air cool. Clouds also block outgoing radiation from Earth, retaining warmth in the air, particularly at night. Clouds rarely form over desert regions, so deserts get very hot during the day but can plunge to near freezing by night.

Different clouds

All clouds form in the lower part of Earth's atmosphere, called the troposphere. There are two main families of clouds, which are classified based on their structure. They are cumulus and stratus clouds. Cumulus clouds look like floating balls of cotton in the sky. They signal unstable weather conditions. Stratus clouds stretch across the sky in layers that look like rippling sheets. Stratus clouds indicate stable weather conditions.

More names are given to clouds based on the height at which they form. Cirrus clouds (or clouds that begin with the term *cirro*) are the highest of all the clouds. Cirrus clouds are found at heights of 16,500 feet (5,000 meters) or more above Earth's surface. Clouds that form in the middle of the troposphere, between 6,500 feet (2,000 meters) and 16,500 feet (5,000 meters), begin with the term *alto*. Clouds that form at the lowest level of the troposphere are called cumulus, stratus, or stratocumulus clouds.

All the different cloud names can be combined to create more names for specific cloud formations. For example, cirrostratus clouds appear high in the troposphere and form a milky-white layer across the sky. Altocumulus, altostratus, and cirrocumulus clouds also exist. By identifying the parts of a cloud's name, one can figure out its location as well as what it looks like.

Some weather forecasters recognize another group of clouds, called nimbus clouds. The word *nimbus* means rain-bearing, so nimbostratus clouds are low-level, rain-bearing clouds that form in thick layers across the sky.

Cumulonimbus clouds form a separate group. These clouds form at the lowest level of the troposphere and grow upward, eventually reaching the upper limit of the troposphere at 60,000 feet (18,000 meters). Cumulonimbus clouds are storm clouds. They often cause thunder and lightning.

See also: RAIN AND RAINFALL • SNOW AND FROST

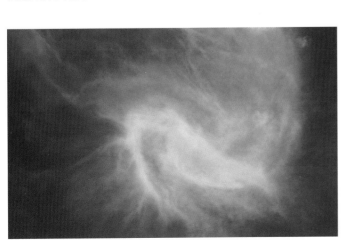

Coal mining

Many great beds of coal deep underground have helped to make the United States the leading industrial nation. Coal is an important fuel for providing power and heating homes. It is also an ingredient in the manufacture of many products.

Most coal was formed between 250 and 400 million years ago. At that time, dense forests and swamps covered much of Earth. The forests were mostly made up of strange trees that looked like giant ferns. As the plants died, they fell into the swamps and rotted. After a long time, they turned into peat, a substance that is still dried and burned as fuel in some countries. Then the land sank and was covered by more layers of peat, and then by rivers and seas. The great pressure of the overlying sediments and the oceans squeezed the peat even more until, after millions of years, it turned into coal. Great coal beds, called seams, lay undisturbed underground until people discovered them.

About 1200 CE, a monk near Liège in Belgium wrote that he had seen black earth being burned as fuel. From the thirteenth to the sixteenth centuries, the area around Liège was famous for its coal. Shafts were dug into the hills overlooking the town to get at the valuable fuel.

In England, coal was first mined in the Middle Ages (500–1500 CE). By the time of Queen Elizabeth I (1533–1603), London had begun to import coal from the north of England, and from then until the late nineteenth century, Britain was the chief coal-producing country in the world.

In the United States, coal was not mined on a commercial scale until the middle of the eighteenth century. The first coal mines were at Richmond, Virginia, but coal was not an important fuel in the United States until the middle of the nineteenth century. This was because of the abundance of wood from the vast forests. Wood remained the main fuel until after the American Civil War (1861–1865).

Early coal mines

As mines went deeper and deeper, life for the miners became more dangerous. Separate ventilation shafts had to be dug, but the air underground was still dangerous to work in. Birds were taken into mines because they use oxygen faster than people. If there was not enough air, the birds would die in time to warn the miners.

Another problem was flammable methane gas, which is given off by coal when it is cut. This gas can cause fatal explosions. In the early days, a miner would wrap himself in wet rags and crawl along the shaft, holding a burning torch on a long pole ahead of him. The torch would set fire to and burn any gas, and the mine was then safe. Safety measures in mines are now very strict, but mining accidents still happen occasionally.

▲ Miners in South America mine an underground coal face with a pneumatic drill. Much of the machinery used is far larger and more automated. Underground mining is dirty, hard, and often dangerous work.

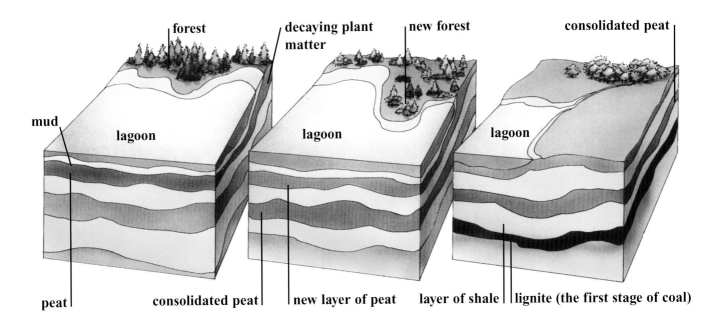

forest   decaying plant matter   new forest   consolidated peat

mud   lagoon   lagoon   lagoon

peat   consolidated peat   new layer of peat   layer of shale   lignite (the first stage of coal)

▲ The formation of coal takes millions of years. It first takes the form of peat, then becomes coal with the effects of pressure and heat.

Types of coal

There are two main kinds of coal: bituminous and anthracite. Bituminous coal is the most common type. Anthracite, or hard coal, is harder, blacker, and shinier. Anthracite was formed from bituminous coal when great pressures developed underground during the creation of mountain ranges. Most of America's anthracite is mined in eastern Pennsylvania. When it burns, anthracite gives off very little smoke.

However, most coal used in the United States is bituminous. It provides fuel for the steel industry and is used in large quantities in factories that generate electricity. The main bituminous coal beds are west of the Appalachian Mountains.

MINING COAL

Coal is mined by two distinct methods: surface mining and underground (deep) mining. Which method is chosen depends on the depth and slope of the coal seam, the surface material, and the value of the land that the mine is on.

Surface mining

Surface mining is carried out by stripping away the surface soil and rock that lies on top of the coal. When the coal seam is exposed, it is often broken up by explosives and loaded by power shovels into huge trucks. Big excavating machines have also been developed, which can quickly strip several hundred feet of surface material without the need for explosives. The loading buckets on these giant machines can scoop up several hundred tons of coal with each operation.

A special mining technique called augur mining can also be used. When the coal has been exposed, huge rotary drills 3 to 7 feet (1 to 2 meters) in diameter bore into the coal seam for some 300 feet (90 meters). The cut coal travels back along the drill and is collected at the mouth of the hole.

The costs of surface mining are low compared with underground mining. For that reason, surface mining is used wherever possible. In the United States, nearly half the coal is mined in this way.

Underground mining

Most of the world's coal comes out of underground mines. Some of these mines are as much as 4,000 feet (1,200 meters) deep, but in the United States they are seldom as much as 1,500 feet (460 meters) deep. In deep mines, access to the coal seams is through vertical shafts fitted with hoisting machinery. In shallower mines, the workings may be connected to the surface by sloping tunnels.

▲ **This is a large open-cast surface mine at Leipzig, Germany. Surface coal beds leave enormous scars on the landscape.**

▶ **A large, automated excavating machine is being used at an underground coal face. These machines can produce many tons of coal every hour.**

In small mines of this kind, the miners can walk to their work areas. In larger slope mines, they travel to the coal seam in small, covered railroad cars.

Deep mining methods

There are two main methods of underground working: room and pillar, and longwall working. In the room and pillar method, once the coal seam has been reached, tunnels are driven into the seam in two directions at right angles to each other. This divides the seam into a number of rectangular blocks of coal (the pillars). The pillars of coal, which act as roof supports, vary in size and shape. They may be anything from 30 feet (9 meters) square to 150 by 300 feet (45 by 90 meters).

Machines have been developed for digging these horizontal tunnels. In one minute, they can cut several inches into the coal seam and produce 10 tons (9 tonnes) of coal. The coal is loaded onto conveyors or cars and carried to the surface.

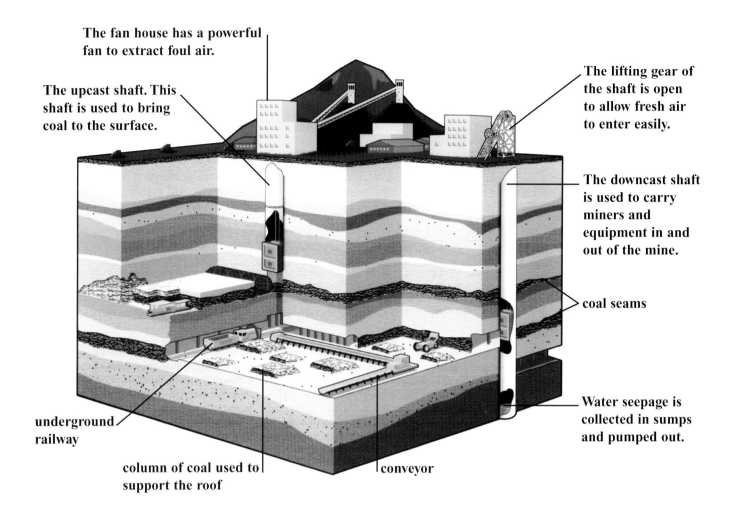

The fan house has a powerful fan to extract foul air.

The upcast shaft. This shaft is used to bring coal to the surface.

The lifting gear of the shaft is open to allow fresh air to enter easily.

The downcast shaft is used to carry miners and equipment in and out of the mine.

coal seams

Water seepage is collected in sumps and pumped out.

underground railway

column of coal used to support the roof

conveyor

▲ *This illustration show a typical underground coal mine (not drawn to scale). Usually, much of a coal seam must be left in place to support the rock layers above. Long-wall mining, however, removes the whole seam and lets the roof fall into the remaining space.*

In longwall working, all the coal is extracted from an area. There are no pillars left in the seam. Two parallel tunnels are driven into the seam, some 150 to 700 feet (45 to 200 meters) apart. These tunnels are then joined by another tunnel at right angles. It is this cross tunnel that forms the longwall coal face.

Automatic machines cut the coal from the longwall, and the mined coal is carried by conveyor to one of the parallel entry tunnels to be brought out of the mine. A system of self-advancing roof supports can be used to hold up the roof above the mined-out areas. As the coal is cut away and the longwall face moves forward, the roof behind the face is allowed to collapse. Coal faces like this can advance several yards (meters) a shift and produce 7,000 tons (6,350 tonnes) in a day. It is possible for all these operations to be controlled by one person stationed well away from the cutting area.

Grading and washing

Coal straight from the mine comes in pieces of different sizes and is mixed with rock and dirt. It must be graded and cleaned before it can be used. The largest lumps of coal are passed under rollers that break them down, and the coal passes over a number of screens. The holes in each screen are increasingly larger, and in this way the coal is graded for size. After being graded, the coal is often washed in a tank with running water. The water takes away most of the dirt.

See also: MINING AND QUARRYING

Cog railroad

Ordinary trains are not very good at climbing hills. A locomotive's wheels cannot grip the railroad tracks properly if it has to climb more than a gentle slope. The weight of the coaches behind the locomotive make it slip and roll backward. The cog railroad was developed to solve this problem.

Today it is normal to limit the steepness of climb of railroad tracks. For main lines, the limit is 1 foot upward for every 35 feet forward (30.5 centimeters for every 10.7 meters). For smaller railroad lines, which do not carry such heavy train loads, the steepness can be no more than 1 foot upward for every 20 feet forward (30.5 centimeters for every 6.1 meters). This means that a main line railroad cannot climb more than 150 feet in height for each mile it travels forward (29 meters in height per kilometer). Therefore, if a railroad is needed to go up any steep hill or mountain, ordinary locomotive wheels running on ordinary rails will not be able to do the job.

The rack-and-pinion system

One way of solving this problem is to build a cog railroad. These railroads use a rack-and-pinion system to make sure that trains can keep a firm grip on the rails as they haul themselves uphill.

The rack is an extra rail, laid alongside the normal rails. But instead of being smooth and flat, it has teeth (notches). The pinion is a special cog wheel, fitted on locomotives and sometimes on the cars, too. As the locomotive moves along the track, the teeth of the rack and the teeth of the pinion engage (fit in) with each other, stopping the train from slipping backward. The rack and pinion (or pinions) can either be arranged vertically, or horizontally, as in the illustrations on page 351.

▼ *Mount Washington cog railroad in New Hampshire was the first mountain cog railroad. Opened in 1869, it uses a vertical rack-and-pinion system.*

The first rack railroad

The idea of the cog system was developed around 1812, at the same time as steam trains themselves were being pioneered. John Blenkinsop, the manager of Middleton colliery in England, laid a rack rail along the track used for hauling coal trucks, and fitted pinion wheels to the locomotives.

However, Blenkinsop was overcautious. His line was not very steep and did not need a rack rail at all. The weight of the locomotive itself, bearing down on its driving wheels, gave enough grip. This proved that iron wheels on iron rails were safe for gentle slopes. When railroad engineers realized this, they lost interest in rack systems for many years. The idea became popular again when railroad engineers needed to build mountain railroads.

Early mountain railroads

In 1869, the first mountain cogged railroad was laid up the side of Mount Washington in New Hampshire. Two years later, Europe's first mountain cog railroad was opened, traveling up and down Mount Rigi in Switzerland. Since then, a number of cogged lines were laid, mainly in Europe, to take trains through or up mountain areas, or up steep industrial sites.

▲ The Mount Pilatus cog railroad in Switzerland is the steepest in the world. It uses the Locher system, with horizontally mounted pinion wheels on either side of a double-edged rack.

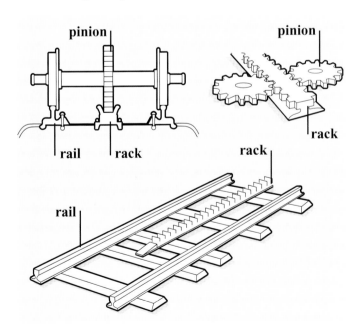

▲ The pinion on a rack railcar is physically attached to the rack rail on the ground, either vertically (top left) or horizontally (top right).

Vertical systems are safe on climbs up to 1 in 4 steep (one unit of distance up for every four along), but some climbs are steeper. The Mount Pilatus line in Switzerland has an amazing 1 in 2 climb. These climbs employ the Locher horizontal system. This system uses a rack with teeth on either side instead of on top, and horizontally mounted pinion wheels on each side to drive and brake the cars.

Modern mountain railroads

As steam locomotives are now disappearing, so too are cog railroads, which are slow and costly to build and run. Travelers now more often climb mountains by means of cable cars.

See also: CABLE TRAVEL • GEAR

Communications satellite

Space research has led to the age of the communications satellite and instant long-distance communication. Some radio signals and all television signals are blocked by the curve of Earth and even by mountains. But signals sent up to a satellite in space and bounced back to Earth avoid these obstacles. These signals can travel freely from continent to continent.

The first live television pictures were exchanged between the United States and Europe by the satellite *Telstar I* in 1962. Since then, hundreds of satellites have been launched. Today, live broadcasts from one continent to another occur every day, and communications satellites handle millions of telephone calls at a time.

Why do we need satellites?

Radio signals can travel much farther than television signals. They can do so because of an invisible layer called the ionosphere in the upper atmosphere. The layer is made up of electrically charged particles, and radio signals in the long, medium, and short wave bands bounce off it back to Earth. In fact, they bounce up and down between Earth and the ionosphere until they go right around Earth, growing weaker as they travel.

Television broadcasts, however, must be transmitted on the ultra high frequency (UHF) and very high frequency (VHF) wavebands. These very short waves go right through the ionosphere and are not reflected back to Earth. So it is impossible to broadcast television pictures farther than the horizon. Even with a tall transmitting mast set on a high point of land, signals cannot travel much farther than 150 miles (250 kilometers). Therefore, satellites in space are needed to bounce back the television signals to Earth.

▲ *A U.S. soldier sets up a mobile satellite phone to allow him to communicate to his commanders. Ordinary radios often do not work in remote locations.*

Positioning satellites

The first television transmission between the United States and Europe in 1962 lasted only a few minutes because the satellite that was used, *Telstar I*, was in a low orbit around Earth. The satellite rushed across the sky and soon disappeared over the horizon, making further transmission impossible.

Modern communications satellites are placed in a high orbit—22,300 miles (35,880 kilometers) above Earth. At this height, they take exactly one day to travel once around Earth. If such a satellite is placed in orbit right over the equator, and is set to travel from west to east, it goes around Earth at exactly the same speed as Earth turns under it. So the satellite appears to remain fixed in the sky, always over the same spot on the equator. This type of orbit is called a geostationary or synchronous orbit. Three such satellites, spaced out around the equator, can give worldwide television coverage, except for areas around the North and South Poles.

The Intelsat communications network begun in the late 1960s is still the world's main satellite system. New satellites are launched regularly from the United States to replace existing ones that have stopped working, usually after seven to ten years in space. Any country can hire time on the Intelsat satellite network, as well as on many others.

Communications satellite design

The satellites used have been improved upon over the years, but basically they all have some things in common. The antennas are "dish" reflectors that gather the incoming signals and focus the outgoing signals into a narrow beam aimed at a particular ground station. Other antennas have a wider beam to cover a larger part of Earth's surface.

Although the antennas remain stationary in relation to a point on Earth, the base of most satellites rotates at a rate of about one revolution per second. It is driven by a small electric motor.

There are two reasons for this rotation of the satellite. The first is that the spinning motion helps stabilize the satellite and keep it from drifting out of position. The spinning motion acts something like a gyroscope (a universally mounted spinning wheel that offers resistance to turns in any direction). The second reason for the spinning is equally important. Anything in space that always keeps the same face toward the Sun gets extremely hot on that side and extremely cold on the other, shaded, side. This is not good for the complicated electronics inside the satellite.

Some more recent satellites do not revolve. They are kept in a stable position by gyroscope systems inside them, and the heating problem is solved by a special outer shell. These satellites have large wing-shaped solar panels that point continuously at the Sun, allowing the satellite to pick up more solar power to work its electronic equipment.

Amplifying the signals

The satellite receives the signals beamed up to it by special ground stations. It then has to amplify (strengthen) the signals some ten thousand million times before sending them back to Earth. The incoming and outgoing signals are on different wavelengths so that there is no chance of their interfering with each other. Microwaves are used. Microwaves are a form of electromagnetic radiation with a short, easily controlled wavelength.

▶ *This is an artist's impression of the European Space Agency's* **Artemis** *satellite.* **Artemis** *is designed to meet the requirements of a wide variety of users. It can operate in different orbits, and it has three sophisticated payloads for the fulfillment of navigational, mobile communication, and data gathering missions. It also has a unique intersatellite link-up capability, which allows it to communicate with other satellites.*

The satellite is powered by solar energy, which comes from its photoelectric cells. Batteries supply current when the Sun is eclipsed by Earth.

Ground stations

On Earth, ground stations are the link between the satellites and the people who use them. There are hundreds of ground stations in the commercial satellite network. This number is growing with demand, especially for mobile telecommunications. The largest of these stations can handle color television and several thousand telephone lines. They have a transmitting power of several thousand watts (kilowatts).

Ground station dish antennas are usually 98 feet (30 meters) across. These big dishes can be moved to point at any satellite within "sight." The same dish antenna is used for both transmitting and receiving signals from the satellites. It is possible to use the same dish because the transmitted and received signals are on different wavelengths.

Other satellite systems

The commercial satellite network is just one of several systems. The United States has at least three separate military satellite networks, not counting its "spy-in-the-sky" surveillance and other military satellite systems.

The Russian Federation also has a large satellite system. As much of the country is in the far north, the Russians prefer an elliptical orbit for their satellites. At their lowest point of orbit, these satellites are only 310 miles (500 kilometers) above Earth, but at their highest they are 24,800 miles (40,000 kilometers) up. The orbits are so arranged that the satellites spend about 8 hours out of 12 high over Siberia, and then they speed rapidly through the rest of the orbit. The antenna dishes on the satellites can be moved so that they are kept pointing at Earth during the satellites' oval orbit.

Weather satellites

There are two main kinds of weather satellites. They are either geostationary or polar orbiting. The polar weather satellites are put into a much lower orbit than the geostationary ones, only about 500 miles (800 kilometers) above Earth. They circle Earth, crossing the equator every two hours or so, and they pass close to the North and South Poles. Each orbit is about 30 degrees longitude farther west than the one before, allowing nearly all the globe to be covered every 12 hours. Polar-orbiting satellites are very useful tools for the weather forecaster because of the excellent pictures they take from their relatively low altitude.

▼ *These satellite dishes, at a ground station in the United States, can move to point at any satellite within their line of "sight" and can send and receive signals.*

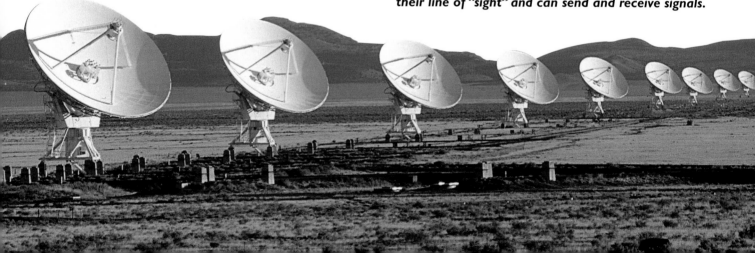

▲ *American astronauts carefully drag the INTELSAT VI communications satellite toward the cargo hold of a space shuttle, where they will perform repairs.*

◄ *The cylinder-shaped MSG-1 is placed onto its payload adaptor, ready for launch in a space shuttle in 2000. The launch was successful, and MSG-1 now provides detailed global weather data for Europe.*

Weather satellites take two types of pictures. An ordinary photograph shows the position of clouds in daytime. But the satellites also take infrared photographs. These photographs measure the temperature of the part of Earth's surface at which the camera is directed. Infrared pictures can be taken in darkness as well as daylight. By studying ordinary photographs and infrared pictures side by side, the forecaster can tell a great deal about weather patterns around the world.

The launching of satellites

Most of the cost of a communications satellite goes into launching it into space. It is hoped, therefore, that as space travel advances, launch costs will be reduced. The space shuttle's large cargo bay has space for several satellites on one flight to help divide costs. The space shuttle can also be used to carry out repairs to satellites in orbit. Some satellites are constructed so that in-flight servicing is possible. It may be cheaper to repair or upgrade an existing satellite than to build and launch a new one.

Spacecraft may also be used for other purposes. At present there are several thousand "dead" pieces of "space junk" circling around and around our planet. Many of these useless pieces of metal are in orbit over the equator, and this satellite route will gradually become more and more congested. As time goes by, more and more of these useless satellites will begin to clutter up space. So it has been suggested that spacecraft could "clean up" space by pushing these unwanted satellites into orbits that would, in time, make them approach the Sun and burn up.

See also: BROADCASTING • MOBILE COMMUNICATION

Compass

By the first century BCE, the Chinese had found out that an iron-rich rock called lodestone would always align itself north-south if it was free to move. Compasses on ships were not developed until several centuries later. Today, the magnetic compass is used for all kinds of navigation.

▲ *In a simple pocket compass, the large pointer has a marked end that will always point to magnetic north. The smaller pointer can be rotated to mark a direction of travel (bearing) for the navigator.*

The magnetic compass was invented in China, and it was originally used as a fortune-telling instrument. However, as the compass shows the directions of north and south, it is very important to navigation. Navigating is being able to determine one's way across land or through air or water. It is not known where or when the magnetic compass was first used for navigation. The earliest written record of its use is by Chinese mariners in 1115 CE.

The first compass consisted of a hollowed-out lodestone (magnetic iron oxide). The lodestone was floated on water, and it always floated on a north-south axis, in line with Earth's magnetic poles. Soon it was learned that any iron could be magnetized, either by stroking it with a lodestone or by keeping it absolutely still during the cooling period of its manufacture. A bar of magnetized iron, therefore, could be used as easily as a lodestone.

The next improvement made by the Chinese was the development of the needle compass. If an iron needle is stroked with a lodestone, it will become magnetized. This magnetized iron needle was balanced on a vertical pivot so that it could swing easily in various directions. Most of these early Chinese compasses, which were usually shaped like a fish, could be used only in calm seas.

Improving design

It is thought that Arab seafarers were using compasses for navigation by the middle of the thirteenth century. Their earliest instruments were also fish-shaped, which may mean that they learned about the compass from China. By the end of the same century, mariners' compasses were in wide use in Europe. By then, important improvements had also been made.

One improvement was to set the compass in gimbal rings, which are a series of pivoted brass rings attached to a base. They keep the compass upright, even when the base pitches in a rough sea.

The second change was to improve the directional markings on the face of the compass. The credit for this is usually given to Flavio Gioia of Italy, around 1300 CE. With the subdivisions north, south, east, and west marked, it was easier to keep on course because the directions could be more exact. This improvement helped make possible the great sea voyages of discovery of the fifteenth and sixteenth centuries.

By the thirteenth century, the directional scale (now called a card) was further refined. As well as the four chief directions—north, south, east, and west (called cardinal points)—compass cards came to be marked in degrees. There were 360 degrees in total: north was at 0 degrees, east at 90 degrees, south at 180 degrees, and west at 270 degrees. This 360-degree circle came from the calculations of astronomers in ancient Babylonia.

Finding magnetic north

Astronomers in the fifteenth century became aware of a difference between true north (the direction of the North Pole) and magnetic north (the direction in which the compass needle points). The difference is called magnetic declination, or variation. This variation can now be found for any locality by consulting charts.

On his second voyage to the Americas in 1493, Columbus carried compasses that had been altered in an attempt to allow for variation.

The modern compass

A modern sailor's compass has a 360-degree card that is 6 to 9 inches (15 to 22.5 centimeters) in diameter. The card rests on a bearing in a bowl filled with liquid. The card carries either a pair of bar magnets or a single ring magnet. A pointer, sticking out from the inside of the bowl in which the compass card rests, gives the sailor a bearing.

The liquid in the compass bowl is usually either a mixture of alcohol and water or a light oil. All the parts of the compass, except the magnets themselves, must be non-magnetic. The compass bowl is suspended on gimbal rings that keep the bowl level regardless of the movements of the ship.

▲ **This is the bridge of the Royal Clipper—one of the largest cruising yachts in the world. The ship's compass is in the brass case in front of the wheel.**

See also: GYROSCOPE • MAGNETISM

Computer

A computer is a machine that follows a set of instructions. These instructions tell the computer how to do a task or solve a problem. It is hard to imagine a world without computers. Many people use personal computers at home, at work, or at school. They are useful for applications such as word processing, managing accounts, and playing games. Computers are also used to control many items people use every day, such as automobiles, dishwashers, and television sets.

In 1947, U.S. computer scientist Howard Aiken (1900–1973) predicted that six electronic digital computers would be needed for the entire United States. Fifty years later, the computer industry had built one billion personal computers, and another billion are expected by 2008.

Computers have had a huge effect on how people go about their lives. On average, each person in the United States uses around 150 computers every day. Computers are all around us—embedded in everything from cellular phones and compact-disc players to watches and washing machines. Most jobs involve computers in some way, whether it is for e-mail or word processing or more directly, for example, in scientific research. It appears that computers will change people's lives in new and unexpected ways for many years to come.

Mechanical computers

Computers have always been made using the best technology available. The first computers worked by hand. The abacus was the first computer. It was invented in Egypt around 500 BCE and used strings and beads to add and subtract numbers by hand.

In the seventeenth century, French mathematician Blaise Pascal (1623–1662) and German mathematician Gottfried Leibniz (1646–1716) built the first mechanical versions of the abacus.

▶ *Surfing the Internet can be lots of fun for the family, but some Web sites contain material that is offensive. Many parents now use filtering programs to block sites that contain violent or sexually explicit images.*

◄ This photograph, taken in 1946, shows technicians checking the complex system of wires connecting the vacuum tubes of the ENIAC calculating machine. U.S. scientists John Presper Eckert, John Atanasoff, and John Mauchly built ENIAC in the 1940s. This early electronic computer was so big, it filled two large rooms at the University of Pennsylvania.

Instead of moving the beads by hand, the new calculating machines had gear wheels that turned disks marked with numbers.

After the Industrial Revolution of the eighteenth century, many factories and farms used machines and engines. This prompted English mathematician Charles Babbage (1791–1871) to develop the idea of an analytical engine. Babbage dreamed of a steam-driven machine, about the same size as a locomotive, that could perform calculations according to instructions fed in on a punched card. Unfortunately, Babbage was too far ahead of his time—the technology to build the analytical engine did not yet exist.

Other designs for mechanical computers did make the production lines. In the 1880s, U.S. mathematician and mechanical engineer Hermann Hollerith (1860–1929) developed a counting machine to process data from the 1890 United States census. Hollerith's system was a huge success, handling the data from 63 million census returns. In 1896, Hollerith formed the Tabulating Machine Company, which later merged with two others to become the International Business Machines Corporation (IBM). IBM is now the largest computer retailer in the world, with an annual revenue of around $20 billion.

Electronic computers

All modern computers work using electronic switches. The first switches were vacuum tubes—fragile glass tubes that look like light bulbs. More recent computers use transistor switches on silicon chips. A modern silicon chip contains millions of transistors in an area the size of a fingernail.

One of the first electronic computers, called Colossus, was built during World War II (1939–1945). Colossus was the brainchild of English mathematician Max Newman (1897–1984) and his colleagues, who worked as code breakers for the British government at Bletchley Park. Code breakers at Bletchley Park had already achieved considerable success when English mathematician Alan Turing (1912–1954) cracked the German Enigma code. Newman turned his attention to another, more complex code, dubbed "Fish" by Allied forces. Fish was reserved for top-secret Nazi military communications. It was generated by a machine called a *Geheimfernschreiber*, which means "secret telegraph." In 1943, Newman designed and built Colossus to break the Fish code.

Colossus was a special-purpose computer. It could not be programmed to do a wide range of tasks. The world's first programmable electronic computer was built in the United States. In 1946,

U.S. scientists John Presper Eckert (1919–1995) and John Mauchly (1907–1980) unveiled ENIAC (Electronic Numerical Integrator and Calculator) at the University of Pennsylvania. ENIAC had around 18,000 vacuum tubes and occupied 1,500 square feet (140 square meters) of floor space. For many years, Eckert and Mauchly were heralded as the founding fathers of modern computing. U.S. scientist John Vincent Atanasoff (1903–1995) should also be included on the list, however. His contribution to ENIAC was recognized in 1973, when a judge overturned Eckert and Mauchly's patent claims to the computer.

In 1947, U.S. physicists John Bardeen (1908–1991), Walter Brattain (1902–1987), and William Shockley (1910–1989) of Bell Telephone Laboratories, New Jersey, developed the first transistor. This invention won them the 1956 Nobel Prize for physics. Transistors quickly replaced vacuum tubes, allowing computers to become much smaller and use less power. IBM built the first commercial computer using transistors in 1960. This computer, the IBM 7090, was the fastest computer of its time.

After the transistor came the silicon chip. A silicon chip contains many electronic components, such as transistors and capacitors. In 1971, Intel Corporation started selling the Intel 4004. This silicon chip contained all the parts needed for a computer. About the size of a fingernail, the Intel 4004 was as powerful as ENIAC.

▲ *Two giants of the computer industry: Steve Jobs from Apple Computer (left) and William Gates from Microsoft (right).*

Personal computers

Personal computers, or PCs for short, are now the most common computers. PCs are small, relatively cheap, and are used by one person at a time. The invention of the PC has spawned a computer revolution. Today, PCs are essential business tools. Many people also use PCs at home.

The first widely available PC, the Altair 8800, was made in 1974. It had an Intel processor that was programmed by flicking switches on the front of the computer. The first people to buy the Altair 8800 were mainly computer hobbyists. Some of these people are now the owners of multibillion-dollar business empires selling their own PCs and computer programs.

The PC industry began in 1977 when U.S. corporation Apple Computer started selling the Apple II. This was the first computer that was both cheap to buy and easy to use. Apple soon became popular in homes, businesses, and schools throughout the world.

In 1981, IBM sold its first PC—the IBM PC. It used an Intel processor and ran on programs designed by Microsoft Corporation. The IBM PC soon became the most popular PC in the world. All PCs are now named after IBM's original PC.

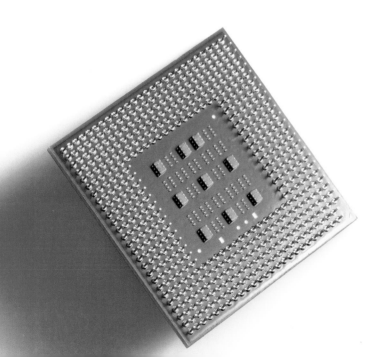

◀ *Intel Corporation's Pentium® 4 microprocessors are some of the most powerful silicon chips on the market. Intel's chips are the brains of 85 percent of the world's personal computers.*

Since the early 1980s, PCs have been based on the IBM or Apple design. A recent Apple computer is the Apple Mac G4 Powerbook, which is around a thousand times faster than the original Apple II. Many other computer manufacturers, such as Hewlett-Packard and Dell now make copies of the IBM PC. It is even possible to build a PC from parts bought from a catalog.

▼ *This picture shows the main components of a typical desktop PC—Hewlett-Packard's Compaq Presario 8000Z. Computer users can add other devices, such as printers and scanners, to the setup.*

How computers work

A set of rules called programs control computers. A simple rule might state something like: if the letter "A" is pressed on the keyboard, put the letter "A" on the screen. The computer program Microsoft Windows XP works using millions of similar rules.

Programs are written by computer programmers and use a language based on English. However, computers work in a different language. Computer programs change the English rules into sequences of numbers that are processed by the computer and then acted upon.

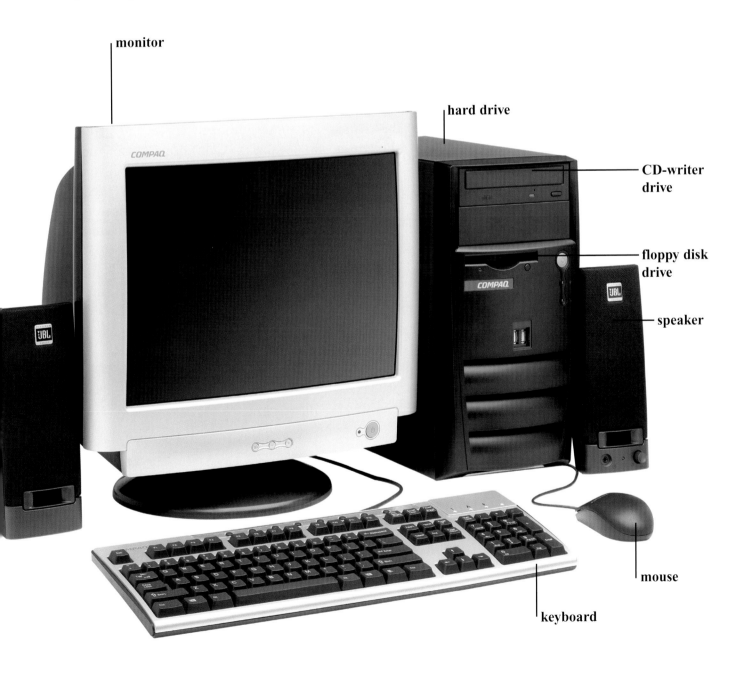

monitor

hard drive

CD-writer drive

floppy disk drive

speaker

mouse

keyboard

Every computer has a central processing unit (CPU). The CPU is the computer's brain and manages all the computer's operations. It inputs a sequence of numbers, performs calculations with the numbers, and then outputs another sequence of numbers. Computer programs then act on the output numbers to make the computer do tasks such as display a letter on the monitor.

Computer counting

When people write or say a number, they use the decimal system of counting. This system is based on the numbers zero (0) through nine (9), which are called the ten decimal digits. The position of the digit represents the amount of ones, tens, hundreds, and so on. For example, the number 632 means six hundreds plus three tens plus two ones.

Computers count with the binary number system. This is based on only two digits, zero (0) and one (1), which are called the two binary digits, or bits for short. The position of the bit represents the amount of ones, twos, fours, eights, and so on—for example, 10101 in binary is sixteen plus four plus one, or 20 in decimal. It is also useful to group eight bits into a byte that can count up to 11111111, or 255 in decimal.

Computers count in binary because the CPU consists of many tiny electronic switches. When a switch is off, the computer counts a zero. When a switch is on, the computer counts a one. Any machine that works by on-and-off signals or switches is called a digital machine. Almost all digital machines have computer chips inside them.

Computers inside and out

There are three main parts in a typical PC: the central processing unit (CPU), the memory, and the input/output (I/O) devices. These components are connected to an electronic circuit board, called the motherboard, either by a slot inside the computer or an outside port into which a cable fits.

The CPU does the calculations that make the computer work. The power of a CPU is described by the size of numbers that it adds and how quickly it adds them. A modern 32-bit CPU adds numbers with 32 binary digits, or up to about four billion in decimal numbers. A typical CPU might add two billion of these numbers per second. It is said to have two Gigahertz (GHz) of processing power.

A computer's memory is where it stores the results of calculations from the CPU. There are two types of memory. Random-access memory (RAM) stores temporary information that the computer is currently using. Read-only memory (ROM) is permanent memory for important information that never changes. The amount of memory a computer has is measured in bytes. Each byte can

▶ *Apple Computer has built on its reputation for innovative industrial design with the release of its PowerBook G4 range of laptop computers.*

store a number from 0 to 255. A modern computer could have 512 million bytes, called 512 megabytes (MB), of RAM storage.

Another type of memory is the computer's permanent storage space on its hard drive. This space stores information such as programs and documents. Unlike RAM memory, storage space is kept after the computer is turned off. It is also slower to use. A typical hard disk might hold 100 gigabytes (GB), or 100 billion bytes, of information.

I/O devices, or peripherals, let people interact with computers. Information enters the computer through input devices and leaves through output devices. All PCs have a keyboard and mouse for entering information and a monitor for displaying the output. Another way of transferring information is through a removable storage device, such as a floppy disk, compact disc (CD), or digital video disc (DVD). Like the computer's hard drive, these devices store information, although the discs can also be inserted and removed. Most commercial programs now come on CD or DVD.

There are many different I/O devices. Printers translate the information from computer files, such as a letter, and print it onto paper. Scanners copy words and pictures on paper and convert them into a computer file. Modems enable people to swap information from computer to computer through a phone line. New devices are invented all the time as people find more uses for computers. It is now even possible to connect a television, mobile phone, and digital camera to a PC.

▲ **The tablet PC is a lightweight version of a laptop PC in the shape of a flat panel. People use a penlike device to input information by tapping and writing on the screen. Tablet PCs also let people connect to the Internet and access other PCs.**

Types of computers

Computers come in many different shapes and sizes depending on their use. Some fill rooms, while others fit inside a cell phone. As computers become more useful, the types of computers become steadily more diverse. Few people today are aware of the many computers that make our lives easier.

PCs are the most familiar computer. They are designed for one person to use at a time. Most PCs come in one of two designs. Desktop computers

◄ **IBM's ASCI White supercomputer is about 40,000 times more powerful than an average desktop computer. This supercomputer is housed at the U.S. Department of Energy's Lawrence Livermore National Laboratory in California. It is used to help ensure the safety and reliability of the U.S. nuclear weapons stockpile.**

◄ Customer service representatives input information into their PCs. Every PC is linked to a network so that everyone in the company has access to all the data. Office workers use PCs for many different tasks, from data entry to desktop publishing.

have a separate keyboard, mouse, and monitor. Laptops, or notebooks, come in one portable package. Businesses rely on desktop PCs and laptops for accounting, desktop publishing (DTP), managing company information on databases, and word processing. The most popular uses for PCs at home are playing games and surfing the Internet.

Handheld computers are portable computers that are small enough to hold in your hand. Other names for handheld computers include palmtops, pocket computers, and personal digital assistants (PDAs). As their name suggests, handheld computers come in one package and are small enough to be carried around. Since they are so small, most handheld computers do not have a keyboard. People input information into the computer using an electric penlike device to tap and write onto the screen. The most popular uses of handheld computers are as personal organizers and address books.

Embedded computers are tiny computers found inside many common appliances, from dishwashers and digital watches to microwave ovens and MP3 players. They make life much easier by making everyday items simple to use. Embedded computers are the most common type of computer, but most people are unaware of them. There are already more embedded computers on the planet than there are people, and they are becoming more widespread every day.

Mainframes are large, fast, and expensive computers that many people use at one time. Typically, they will fill a room and cost millions of dollars. Their main use is in banks, industry, and for scientific research.

Supercomputers are the fastest and most expensive computers. Their speed and power is phenomenal, some performing tens of trillions of calculations every second. Supercomputers are used for specialized problems that need huge amounts of calculating power, for example, nuclear research and weather forecasting.

Computer networks

A computer network is a group of linked computers that can exchange information. Computer networks allow people to send e-mails and access documents or programs on another computer. Several computers on the same network can also share common peripherals, such as printers and scanners.

There are two basic types of networks—local-area networks (LANs) and wide-area networks (WANs). LANs connect several computers together so they can use the same printers or, perhaps, a large information store, called a server. WANs connect

---

DID YOU KNOW?

The first computer programmer was English mathematician and musician Augusta Ada King, Countess of Lovelace (1815–1852), the daughter of English poet Lord Byron (1788–1824). Countess Lovelace spent many years working with Charles Babbage developing the analytical engine. She developed many programs for his machine but unfortunately died before a working computer could be constructed.

computers and LANs over large networks that span countries or entire continents. LANs use cables to connect each computer to the network. WANs typically use a modem and phone line.

The Internet is the largest network of computers. It connects millions of computers throughout the world. The amount of information on the Internet is staggering. Everyone can access this information from anywhere in the world as long as they have a computer, modem, and phone line.

The user interface

People interact with computers through the user interface. Most computers work using a graphical user interface (GUI), which is a collection of symbols, called icons, on the computer monitor. These icons represent the documents and programs on a computer. GUIs are designed to be used with a mouse, which is a handheld device for moving a pointer around on the screen. The combination of a mouse and GUI is a simple way of making computers accessible for everyone.

GUIs are an example of software—a collection of programs that the computer uses to do specific tasks. Software consists of a list of instructions telling the computer what to do. People called computer programmers write the instructions in a language that the computer understands.

There are two types of software—system software and application software. System software, or the operating system, makes the computer work and contains the main GUI. Most people use either Microsoft Windows, Linux, or the Mac OS (for Apple Computers). Application software is the collection of programs that are used to do tasks. Examples include Apple's Safari for surfing the Internet, Microsoft Word for word processing, and computer games such as Primal.

Benefits of computers

Computers are a central part of everyday life. Almost everyone who lives in an industrialized country uses computers. CD players, cell phones, dishwashers, and most other modern-technology items have embedded computers inside them.

▲ **This picture is from the Microsoft Windows XP graphical user interface. People can access files, open applications, or surf the Internet using a mouse to click on the relevant icons.**

Most modern-technology items are designed with computer-assisted design (CAD) software and are made in factories with robotic assembly lines. Stores take the money for purchases using computerized registers, while the money is taken from a bank account that is stored on a computer database. Recently, people have also been using the Internet to shop from the comfort of their homes.

Telecommunications technology, such as cellular phones, uses digital signals that are controlled by computers. These digital signals are beamed around the world by satellites, which are also controlled by computers. With this technology, it is now possible to communicate from almost anywhere in the world.

Many physical disabilities can be aided by computer technology. There are artificial limbs, speech synthesizers, and wheelchairs operated by computer. These devices give people with physical or mental disabilities independence and control over their lives.

Scientists use computer technology to analyze and make models of data. Simulation programs can predict weather conditions for meteorologists, test prototype airplanes and automobiles, and design new medicines and drugs.

365

◄ *People with mental and physical disabilities can now enjoy playing computer games, thanks to technology such as brain-activated systems. Sensors connected to this boy's fingers monitor electrical signals in his skin, as well as signs such as heartbeat and body temperature. The sensor then translates these signals into actions on the computer monitor.*

Another use of computers is as learning aids. Educational software presents information in an interactive way. Recently, high schools and colleges have also started training students in traditional application programs such as word processing, databases, spreadsheets, and DTP.

Problems with computers

Computers are machines, so they can break down. If a hard disk fails, all of the information stored by the computer is lost. This can be catastrophic for businesses that rely on computers. To prevent this from happening, many businesses have automated backup systems that copy important information to an external storage device when the office closes each night.

There is also a growing digital divide between people who have access to computers. Those who own computers find them easy to use and extremely beneficial. Those who are not familiar with computers can find them intimidating and thus miss out on jobs and entertainment.

Malicious programs that harm computers and destroy data are another growing problem. The widespread use of e-mail software has spawned a number of different computer viruses. Viruses are programs that move from computer to computer, infecting each one as it moves on. Viruses can damage computer hardware or access confidential information, such as credit-card details. Trojan horses are another danger. They are disguised to look like harmless software, but if they are used they can be extremely harmful. Trojan horses can allow a stranger to look through someone's computer without the owner knowing.

Criminals are using computers for a new type of crime, called cybercrime. The Federal Bureau of Investigation (FBI) estimates that there is about $10 billion of cybercrime every year. Cybercrimes include credit-card fraud across the Internet, e-mail scams, and cyberterrorism. Cyberterrorists could overload telephone lines, disrupt air-traffic control, and scramble the software used by banks and the emergency services.

The future of computing

In 1965, the cofounder of Intel Corporation, Gordon Moore (1929–), made his famous prediction that the processing power and memory of computers would double every 18 months. This law, now called Moore's law, has been true for the last 30 years. Moore's law has become the guiding principle for the computer industry to deliver increasingly powerful semiconductor chips at proportionate decreases in cost.

By the year 2020, the circuits on computer chips will be the size of atoms. Current techniques for making computer chips will no longer work. New materials and techniques will have to be used to make more powerful computers. One possibility is quantum computers that work following the rules of quantum physics, which describe atoms and molecules. Quantum computers could perform tasks that are impossible to do using conventional computers, such as instantly searching through vast amounts of information.

New uses will be thought of for the powerful computers of the future. Already, computers can make virtual-reality settings. The computer simulates a three-dimensional world that is seen through goggles. Gloves allow the items in this world to be held or moved. In the future, these virtual-reality worlds will be completely realistic, opening up a new generation of computer games and realistic training simulations.

▲ *A boy wearing a virtual-reality helmet plays a video game in an amusement arcade. As well as computer games, virtual-reality technology has been applied to building simulations, spaceflight, and medical training.*

DID YOU KNOW?

In the future, it may be possible to make a computer from deoxyribonucleic acid (DNA). This material stores the genetic code for almost every living organism on Earth. A DNA computer would be billions of times more powerful than any modern computer. DNA molecules have already been used to solve difficult mathematical problems. Many scientists believe that DNA chips would be able to unravel the complex mysteries of life and produce a host of new drugs.

Another use of computer power is artificial intelligence (AI), in which computers do tasks that require humanlike intelligence. These tasks include playing games like chess, recognizing handwriting, understanding speech, speaking a language, making medical diagnoses, and many more. As computers become more powerful, AI systems will start to replace people for many everyday tasks.

Many AI systems are designed as neural networks—computer programs that work in a similar way to the human brain. These neural networks can do many things that are currently done by people, such as learning and reasoning. The human brain is made of around ten billion neurons with several thousand connections to each neuron. If a computer were to have a similar neural network, it could be as intelligent or even more intelligent than a person.

Although it is impossible to predict the future, one thing is certain—computers will continue to change people's lives in new and exciting ways. Technology has greatly improved over the last 30 years, and it will continue to do so in the future.

See *also*: ARTIFICIAL INTELLIGENCE • BABBAGE, CHARLES • COMPUTER GRAPHICS • INTERNET • PRINTING • SCANNER, IMAGE • SILICON • TRANSISTOR • VIRUS, COMPUTER

Computer graphics

Believe it or not, the characters in *Shrek* and *Toy Story*, Jar Jar Binks in *Star Wars,* and Gollum in the movie version of *The Lord of the Rings* are all just a bundle of triangles and other geometric shapes. They have more in common with a character from a cereal box than with real actors. These characters were all created using computer graphics. But how does what you see on a computer make it to the big screen?

The science of computer graphics these days appears deceptively simple to the computer user. Most of the work is done behind the scenes by the computer's processor (CPU), a microchip that performs millions of calculations a second. Every time the computer mouse moves across the desk, the CPU calculates where it is going and moves a corresponding pointer on the screen. If you are using a software application for painting, you click with the mouse and drag the pointer to draw a line. The processor is merely doing more calculations to make that line appear on the screen.

Computer graphics are just a collection of these lines drawn on the computer screen. It is the skill of the artist and the power of the software applications that turn these simple lines into the animated characters that fill our movie screens.

Different dimensions

Computer graphics can be divided into two categories—two-dimensional (known as 2D) and three-dimensional (3D). The third dimension in three-dimensional graphics is depth, which is added to the two flat dimensions of horizontal and vertical. 2D graphics are simpler than 3D ones and are more closely related to the action of drawing lines with a mouse.

Two-dimensional graphics

2D graphics software applications can be divided into two types: those derived from sketching and drawing, and those derived from photography. The two types have their own way of representing images on the screen. The drawing applications use vector graphics, basically outlines of shapes created with lines and curves and filled with a color or pattern. Those based on photography use bitmap graphics, which are made up of a grid of tiny colored dots placed on the screen by the computer as the mouse moves. These dots are called picture elements or

◄ *The movie character Shrek was created using computer graphics. A graphic artist is able to draw a character's shape and then add a variety of lifelike effects.*

pixels; when viewed on the computer screen, they display what appears to be a continuous color tone. The grids are of course invisible to the eye, being used only by the processor to place the pixels.

Pixels are the key to bitmap computer graphics, and the way that they are displayed on the monitor affects the quality of the image. The more pixels that can be squeezed into an area of the screen, the clearer and more defined the image becomes. This is measured in dots per inch (dpi). The amount of definition of an image is known as its resolution. A low-resolution image will look blocky, while a high-resolution image will appear crisp.

Resolution is less important when dealing with vector graphics. These images depend on the position and length of the lines and curves that form their structure. These are just numbers that the processor understands and converts into 2D objects of a certain shape and size. As they consist merely of numbers, the shapes can be made bigger or smaller by multiplication and division. Again,

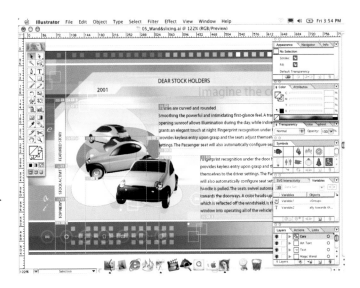

▲ **Adobe Illustrator is a software package that is used to create two-dimensional computer graphic images using vectors. It is used by graphic designers, illustrators, and cartographers.**

this is all carried out invisibly by the computer, leaving the monitor to display shapes and images in a form that we can understand.

Three-dimensional graphics

The other category of computer graphics also uses lines and curves in a similar manner. Three-dimensional graphics applications are more complex and require an understanding of how the real world works.

The digital world that these applications operate within is known as 3D space. With the added dimension of depth, 3D space closely mirrors the world we live in. Just as in 2D, lines are important. One of the building blocks of 3D graphics is the polygon, which is a shape made up of at least three lines, such as a triangle or a cube. Several polygons can be joined together to form the surface of objects in 3D—typically spheres, cones, cubes, and so on, which are used to build more complex constructions. Software applications provide tools to manipulate these objects and have the ability to create scenes with interactive models made up of many combined objects. The software can add colors and textures to the surfaces of the models and can provide light and shadow to make the scene look more realistic. Finally, 3D graphics

DID YOU KNOW?

Once vector and bitmap graphics have been created, different file formats are used to save the images. The choice of which format to use is determined by file size. Computers have only a certain amount of storage, known as memory. Image files, especially bitmap images, can take up a lot of memory, so a procedure called compression can be used. The quality of the image depends on how compressed the file is. An image created in Adobe Photoshop will be uncompressed and saved with the file extension .psd; another uncompressed format is .bmp, which is used by Microsoft Paint. Compressed formats are more commonly used because of their small file size. Examples of compressed file extensions are .jpeg, .tiff, and .gif. The last is widely used for Internet graphics.

applications have the ability to animate the scenes and make movies featuring the computer-generated models. The result is what you see on the screen when you watch a movie such as *Shrek*. The green ogre Shrek and his friends, and even the world in which they live, are all just animated scenes created by computer graphics.

Computer graphics in the real world

Not all computer graphics are used for making cartoon characters. The uses to which graphics applications are put are many and varied. Two-dimensional vector graphics software, such as Adobe Illustrator, is widely used in commercial design, for artwork on everything from grocery packaging to posters and signs. Vector graphics are also commonly found on the Internet as flat 2D pictures and logos or in animated form such as Macromedia Flash movies. A designer will spend three or more years learning the basics of art and design before becoming proficient in such creative

tasks. After all, it is the skill of the graphic artist, more than the power of the software, that creates computer graphics.

Artists who work with digital photographs or painting software must be highly skilled as well. Digital images can be taken with a digital camera or brought into the computer using a scanner. Once they are in a digital format, they can be manipulated using software such as Adobe Photoshop. When the designer applies "paint" to a digital photo using a digital brush in Photoshop to hide a spot or change the color of someone's eyes, he or she is really changing the pixels in the bitmap image that the photograph has become. To apply the paint and use the digital tools, the designer will use a mouse or graphics tablet. This tablet is a pressure-sensitive board on which the designer draws with an electronic pen.

Some bitmap graphics software applications also let designers paint using a variety of materials, all replicated by the computer. Corel Painter, for

▶ *The character Jen and her monster friend Scree, from the computer game Primal, are examples of 3D computer graphics. Graphics in computer games must have the ability to move in many different ways, according to inputs from the game player.*

▼ *3D Studio MAX is one of the most widely used 3D graphics software packages. The program can model forms or characters, render (surface) them, add textures, colors, and effects, and animate the results.*

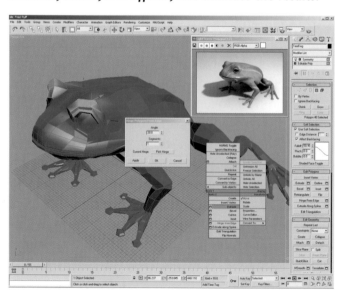

▲ *Gollum, a character from the movie series* **The Lord of the Rings,** *is computer generated, but animators also used the movements of an actor to create the character and make it move in a realistic way.*

example, has a whole digital palette of substances including watercolor paints, ink, airbrushes, chalk and crayon, as well as some unusual materials like liquid metal and even a brush that can spray seashells or flowers onto a digital canvas.

Another type of designer is one who is engaged in drafting architectural, engineering, or mechanical projects. This type of design is generally called computer aided design, or CAD for short. Most, if not all, products and machines today are designed in this way. The CAD designer uses 3D graphics applications to construct machine parts in the computer. Again, these are just objects made up of lines, curves, and polygons that can be assembled to let the designers see how the finished mechanism will look and operate.

Computer games are produced in a similar way. Designers use applications like Alias|Wavefront Maya or Discreet 3D Studio MAX to create games such as Primal for the Sony PlayStation 2 or Tomb Raider for personal computers. These games are again made up from scenes, objects, and models containing thousands of polygons, which are colored and lit. The difference is that these objects are then animated to respond to the movement or commands entered by a joystick, gamepad, or keyboard. The computer processor must do all the calculations to draw the objects on the screen each time they move and must also make sure that the color and lighting moves with the object in a realistic way. This takes up a lot of processing power, so sometimes the computer will also contain a graphics accelerator to help with the calculations.

The special effects wizards who create Shrek, Jar Jar Binks, Gollum, and others use very powerful computers that are dedicated to working with the millions of polygons needed to create characters in animated movies. Often it will take many talented artists several months to animate just one of these characters, painstakingly creating expressions on faces and realistic movement. The software is similar to that used in games development, but the quality of models and animation is much better. And it all starts with a bundle of lines and polygons.

See also: ANIMATION • COMPUTER • SCANNER, IMAGE • SOFTWARE

Copernicus, Nicolaus

Nicolaus Copernicus is considered to be the founder of modern astronomy. Copernicus studied the movements of Earth and the other planets and came to the conclusion that they all move in circles around the Sun. Copernicus's theory, called the Copernican model, was extremely controversial. It had a profound effect on science and philosophy for hundreds of years.

Nicolaus Copernicus was born on February 19, 1473, in Toruń in eastern Poland. His father, Nicolaus, was a prosperous merchant, and his mother, Barbara Watzenrode, also came from a family of wealthy merchants. In 1483, Copernicus's father died, and his uncle, Lucas Watzenrode (1447–1512), saw to his nephew's education and upbringing. From 1491 to 1494, Copernicus attended the University of Kraków, where he studied mathematics and classics. He left before completing his degree but resumed his studies in Italy, at the universities of Bologna and Padua. Copernicus studied a range of subjects—law, Greek, and medicine—but his true interest lay in astronomy. At the University of Bologna, Copernicus was taught by Domenico Maria de Novara (1454–1504), the principal astronomer at the university. Novara was an important influence on the young Copernicus. By helping Novara with his astronomical observations, Copernicus became familiar with the practical methods of astronomy. Novara also introduced Copernicus to the ideas of Greek thinker Claudius Ptolemy (2nd century CE). In 1503, Copernicus received his doctorate in canon law. He returned to Poland shortly after.

▶ A portrait of Nicolaus Copernicus, the Polish astronomer who shocked the world with his idea that the planets, including Earth, circle the Sun.

During Copernicus's time in Italy, Lucas Watzenrode, now Bishop of Ermeland, arranged for his nephew to be made canon of Frauenburg Cathedral. This post gave him an income for life and took up little of his time, so he was able to devote himself to astronomy. In particular, he observed the movements of the Sun, the Moon, and the planets. He tried to predict their positions in the future but found it impossible to do so using the system devised by Ptolemy. In this system, Earth was the fixed center of the universe. The planets, the Sun, and the Moon were thought to orbit (move around) Earth.

Revolutionary ideas

Along with other scientists, Copernicus became increasingly dissatisfied with the Ptolemaic system. Looking back through the work of other ancient Greek astronomers, he found that some had suggested a system with the Sun at the center and the planets orbiting it. Using his own observations,

▲ This illustration of the Copernican system, dating from 1708, shows the planets moving in circles around the Sun. Later astronomers showed that the planets move in oval-shaped paths rather than circles.

Copernicus calculated that Earth was not fixed—it actually moved around on its axis each day and, with the other planets, moved around the Sun.

In 1514, Copernicus sent a pamphlet describing his ideas to a few scholars, but he was reluctant to publish them. Copernicus's suggestion that Earth was just one of many planets orbiting the Sun was revolutionary, and his ideas were considered to be dangerous to the faith of the Catholic Church. Eventually, Copernicus published his theories in a book, *On the revolutions of the celestial spheres,* in 1543, the year of his death. The book was banned by the Catholic Church until 1835.

The Copernican system caused questions to be asked in many areas of science. For example, it was thought that objects fell to Earth because Earth was the center of the universe. If it was not the center, then why did objects fall? Isaac Newton eventually answered this question with his theory of gravity.

See also: ASTRONOMY • SOLAR SYSTEM

Copper

Copper is a soft, orange-brown metal. It was one of the first metals to be used by humans. It is probable that this attractive and useful metal was being beaten into tools and weapons at least 8,000 years ago. Copper is still one of the most versatile and widely used of all the metals.

Most of the world's copper is used in the electrical industry. This reddish metal is the second best conductor of electricity of all the metals. The best is silver, but silver is far too expensive to make into miles of electrical wire for homes and factories.

Copper is also a good conductor of heat. For this reason, it is used in such things as cooking pots and pans, refrigerators, and radiators. Also, copper does not rust, so it is in great demand for fittings that will be exposed to water or to the weather. Copper pipes are used in water systems, and copper containers are used for holding all kinds of liquids.

Copper has other useful properties, too. It is very ductile, which means that it can be stretched, or drawn into very thin wires without breaking. A bar of copper 4 inches (10 centimeters) across can be heated and pulled until it is thinner than a hair.

The other main use for copper is in making the alloys (mixtures of metals) brass and bronze. Brass, the most common copper alloy, usually has about 60 to 90 percent copper, mixed with zinc. Bronze is a mixture of copper and tin, with 70 to 90 percent copper.

▶ *Usually copper is found combined with an element called sulfur in the form of sulfide minerals. Because copper is not a very reactive element, it can also be found, as here, as the pure metal.*

The history of copper

Copper was used by early humans because it was found on the surface of the ground as a ready-made metal. It could be easily beaten into shape for weapons and tools. Copper was probably first used around 8000 BCE by people who lived where Iraq now lies. The early Egyptians used the metal to make ornaments and tools. It was also put to use by the Chinese, Incas, and North American Indians.

Later, before 5000 BCE, people began to smelt (separate by melting) copper from its ores. Ores are rocks that contain a high proportion of a particular mineral. Heat was also used to melt the copper and cast it into useful shapes. By 3500 BCE, the copper and tin alloy bronze had been developed. This important development began the Bronze Age of Europe and Asia.

Copper ores

Copper is widespread on Earth in compounds called carbonates, chlorides, sulfides, and also as the free metal. Copper also forms parts of manganese nodules, which are deposits of the mineral found on areas of the sea floor. These deposits may be crucial when reserves of the metal in Earth's continental crust have been used up.

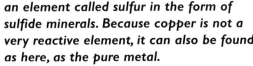

▲ *The enormous Ujina pit at the Collahuasi mine in Chile is one of the largest in the world. The mine contains both copper sulfides and oxides, notably the minerals chalcocite, chalcopyrite, and bornite.*

The distribution of copper results from millions of years of activity on the planet. Molten rock rises within Earth's crust and releases superheated water that dissolves copper minerals and redeposits them within other rocks. Usually the copper combines with sulfur to form sulfide minerals. The most common copper sulfides include chalcopyrite, chalcocite, and bornite. However, copper can also be found combined with other substances. The most significant of these other minerals are the copper oxides, where the copper has combined with oxygen. Examples of copper oxide minerals include cuprite and azurite.

Because copper is not a very reactive mineral, it often can be found as the pure metal. This pure copper, called native copper, was the copper that early humans used.

Nearly all copper used today, though, comes from copper ores, not native copper. As much as 5 tons (4.5 tonnes) of these ores may give as little as 20 pounds (9 kilograms) of copper. The United States is the world's largest producer of copper ore. Arizona, Utah, and Montana produce about three-quarters of the country's supply. Other major copper ore producers include Canada, Chile, Russia, and Zambia.

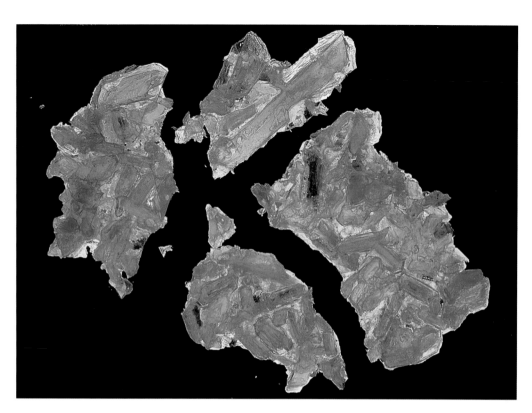

◀ *Copper sulfate is a salt of copper and sulfur and forms striking blue crystals. Copper sulfate is produced in large amounts and is used primarily in agriculture as a fertilizer and as a fungicide.*

▼ *Copper is a good conductor of heat and is widely used to make cooking pots and pans. Copper also resists rusting, which makes it additionally suited for making cooking utensils.*

Getting copper from its ores

Refining copper from its ores is a very complex process, and there are various methods of doing it. With sulfide ores, the rock is first crushed to a powder. Then the powder is put in a water bath with special chemicals, and air is blown through the mixture. Small particles of copper ore cling to the air bubbles and float to the surface of the bath, where they are then skimmed off.

The copper ore that has been skimmed off then goes into a furnace. In the furnace, the impurities rise to the surface and form a waste called slag that is drained off. The remaining ore is metallic copper that is more than 97 percent pure. It can be made purer still by electrolysis. A plate of pure copper and a plate of the impure copper are placed in a tank of copper sulfate ($CuSO_4$) solution and connected to an electrical source. Copper from the positively charged impure plate dissolves into the solution, leaving the impurities behind. The negative, pure plate attracts this extra copper.

Copper is prepared for commercial use in several ways. It can be pulled out into lengths of wire, pressed into rod shapes, or rolled into flat sheets.

See also: ALLOY • BRASS • CASTING • ELECTROLYSIS • IRON AND STEEL • METAL • METALLURGY • METALWORKING

Corrosion

Corrosion is the deterioration of certain metals through contact with oxygen in the atmosphere. This causes a reaction with oxygen, called oxidation. Corrosion can also be caused by chemical action.

When unprotected iron or steel surfaces are exposed to oxygen, especially when in water or a damp atmosphere, they corrode, or rust. Rust is the formation of iron oxide on the surface of a metal containing iron. It has a characteristic orange color, and it is caused by the reaction of oxygen with the iron, in a process called oxidation. Moisture is important in producing the change. In dry conditions, once a layer of iron oxide has formed on the surface, oxygen is prevented from reaching any more of the iron below, and rusting stops. If the surface is damp, however, the coating of rust becomes lumpy and porous (containing holes), and oxygen can continue to react with the iron underneath. Rusting can then continue.

Metals such as aluminum and copper, and alloys (mixed metals) such as brass and stainless steel, may also corrode in certain circumstances. The oxides that form on the surface of these metals are known as patinas. They are less affected by water than rust on iron, and they protect the metals from further corrosion. Sometimes the patinas are even desirable. When copper corrodes, it forms a thin, green patina called verdigris, which is a desirable effect on roofing, for example.

▼ *This scrapyard is full of corroding cars. Most vehicles are made from steel, which contains iron. When iron corrodes, the process is called rusting. This produces a characteristic orange color on the surface of the metal.*

▲ *A painter sprays latex rubber on the nose of an old Sikorsky helicopter. The latex protects the aircraft from moisture and corrosion. The aircraft can be stored outside until they are sold or used for parts.*

Fast and slow corrosion

Corrosion happens everywhere, but it happens at different rates, depending on the climate. In desert regions, iron and steel corrode at a rate of 0.009 thousandths of an inch (0.023 thousandths of a centimeter) per year. In wet tropical regions this figure rises to 21.6 thousandths of an inch (54.9 thousandths of a centimeter) a year.

Preventing corrosion

Provided the corrosion is not too deep, it can be removed from iron and steel by scrubbing with water or by using a polishing powder, but there are various ways to stop it. The surfaces can be painted, or a protective, noncorroding metal coating can be applied. Special anticorrosion paints are used on many metals, especially on iron and steel to protect them from rain or seawater.

Galvanizing is an example of a protective metal coating. In this process, the metal is coated with zinc. Metals can also be chromium plated to prevent corrosion. This produces a shiny finish and is used on many metallic household goods. As a temporary prevention, a film of oil can also be applied to the metal. The oil can be removed when necessary. This method is ideal for protecting machine parts in storage.

See also: COPPER • IRON AND STEEL

Cotton

Cotton is an important natural fiber produced by the cotton plant. It is used in the textile industry and for making other woven materials. Cotton is used in shirts and sails, in bandages and blankets, and in towels and even tea bags. Cotton is grown by over half the countries in the world.

▲ *Cotton plants grow in the southern United States. When ripe, the cotton pods, or burrs, split to reveal the white, fluffy cotton fibers, called bolls.*

Cotton is the seed fiber of a group of plants called *Gossypium*, a member of the Malvaceae family. It is found in most subtropical countries but has been adapted to grow in other conditions. It needs warmth, sun, and plenty of water.

When cotton grows naturally, it can be as tall as 20 feet (6 meters), but as a crop it ranges from 4 to 6 feet (1 to 2 meters). It is usually grown as an annual (having a life cycle of a year). The plants produce creamy-white flowers, which soon turn deep pink and fall off, leaving the small green seed pods, called bolls. Seed hairs or fibers, growing from the outer skin of the seeds, become tightly packed inside the boll. When it is ripe, the boll bursts open to reveal a mass of flufflike fibers. These are white to whitish-yellow, and the main ingredient of the fibers is cellulose.

Harvesting the cotton

When the field takes on the appearance of a field of cotton balls, after all the bolls have burst open, it is time for harvesting. In parts of the world where cotton has grown naturally for centuries, the bolls are still gathered by hand from the dry seed pods (burrs), but machines are normally used by countries that have adapted their agriculture to grow cotton, such as the United States.

The most common types of harvesters are the stripper and the picker. The stripper strips the plant of both opened and unopened bolls, so the cotton has to be further sorted. The picker works by means of a revolving drum with spikes, which pluck the boll out of the burr. The bolls are then removed from the spindles as they turn by a rubber doffer, and compressed air blows them into the basket.

A one-row mechanical picker can do the work of 50 hand pickers. The first successful cotton-picking machine that removed the open bolls and left the burr on the plants was invented in 1927, although it did not come into use until after World War II (1939–1945). Picking machines have vastly increased the production of cotton worldwide.

Cotton manufacture

After harvesting, the cotton must be dried to prevent it from becoming moldy, and it may be placed in a silo (an airtight storage structure) for

▲ *A cotton-picking machine in Texas deposits cotton into a compacting module. Texas produces about 25 percent of the entire U.S. cotton crop and plants over 6 million acres (9,000 square miles) of cotton.*

▶ *Eli Whitney, born in Westboro, Massachusetts, invented the first commercial cotton gin. This machine increased the speed of the process of separating cotton from its burrs and seeds and cleaning it.*

this purpose. Later, the cotton fibers (lint) must be removed from the seed pod in a process called "ginning." This used to be done by hand, although in India a machine called the churcka gin, suitable for the shorter-fibered Indian cotton, was the first known ginning machine to be used.

In 1794, U.S. teacher Eli Whitney (1765–1825) invented a ginning machine suitable for longer-fibered cotton. It had a set of wire teeth set on a revolving cylinder, which drew the lint through a grid without allowing the seeds to pass.

Whitney's cotton gin remained the basic design for gins for a long time. In modern ginneries, the gin stand is often one in a series of machines that finally stack the cotton lint into bales of 400 or 500 pounds (180 or 226 kilograms).

These bales then get sent to spinning mills. At the spinning mills, the matted fibers are cleaned and separated by a machine in what is called the carding operation. The carded fiber, which now resembles a loose rope, is lengthened, straightened, and made thinner in a process called drawing. Fibers to be made into high quality yarn are then combed, removing short fibers and matching the remaining lengths. The spinning process twists the fibers together, making yarn to be wound onto large reels called spools.

The main difference between the groups of cottons is in the length of the fibers. The longest fibers, from the plant *Gossypium barbadense* (called Egyptian and Sea Island cotton), make the finest quality cottons and are the most difficult to grow. They are used in fine fabrics and hosiery. The most common group is *Gossypium hirsutum*, which is grown in the United States and used in the bulk of commercial cottons. The shortest fibers, *Gossypium arboreum* and *Gossypium heraceum,* grown in India, Pakistan, and China, are used to make blankets and carpets.

Pests and diseases

Cotton farmers often lose over 20 percent of their harvest to pests and diseases. That can be even after chemical pesticides have been used, as many pests have developed a resistance to these. The boll weevil and pink bollworm are the most damaging pests. Scientists are trying to develop new pesticides and plants that will resist disease.

Cotton is king

Cotton is one of the world's leading crops, grown in about 60 countries. The four biggest producers are Russia, the United States, China, and India.

Cotton is first known to have been used in 3000 BCE in northwest India. But "King Cotton," as it came to be known, first became important in the nineteenth century with the Industrial Revolution, particularly for the southern states before and during the American Civil War (1861–1865). In the late eighteenth century, cotton provided less than 5 percent of the world's textile raw materials. By 1890 it was nearly 80 percent. Production has nearly doubled since 1930.

Cotton is important because it is so versatile. The fibers can be made into a variety of fabrics, from fine lace to heavy sailcloths. It can be economically produced, and because the twisting operation strengthens the yarn, cotton can also be hard-wearing. It makes a popular fabric because it is comfortable to wear and absorbs perspiration.

Cotton can now be made resistant to stains, water, mildew, and creases. Uses for the very short fibers are disposable clothing, bandages, and teabags. Even those fibers left on the seed after ginning are used in mattresses, quality writing paper, and products that need cellulose, like explosives and plastics. The seed itself is not wasted, either. It yields oil, animal foodstuffs, and fertilizers.

▲ *Pink bollworms emerge from a damaged cotton boll. They are major pests in cotton fields, thriving and multiplying on the cotton plants. If untreated, a crop infested by pink bollworms can be almost entirely lost.*

See also: FIBER • WOOL

Glossary

Amorphous Having no distinct shape—in particular, lacking the structure characteristic of living bodies or without apparent crystalline form.

Antibodies Protective proteins produced by the body's immune system in response to the presence of foreign substances, called antigens.

Antigen A foreign substance in the body that stimulates an immune response.

Atmosphere The layer of gaseous chemicals surrounding Earth. The atmosphere provides oxygen and contains water vapor, which falls as rain. It also protects Earth from harmful radiation and meteors.

Biotechnology The use of microorganisms, such as bacteria, or biological substances, such as enzymes, to produce useful products, such as antibiotics.

Chemical bond The electric forces linking atoms in molecules.

Compound A pure substance consisting of atoms or ions of two or more different elements in definite proportions that cannot be separated by physical means.

Conductor A substance or medium that conducts heat, light, sound, or especially an electric charge.

E-mail An abbreviation of electronic mail, e-mail is a system for sending and receiving messages electronically over a computer network.

Equator The imaginary circle around Earth's surface equidistant from the poles. It divides Earth into the Northern Hemisphere and the Southern Hemisphere.

Focal length The distance from the surface of a lens or mirror to its focal point (the point at which a subject is in focus). Also called focal distance.

Gene A hereditary unit consisting of a segment of deoxyribonucleic acid (DNA). Each gene occupies a specific location on a chromosome (a threadlike body made of DNA in the cell nucleus) and determines a particular characteristic in an organism.

Geometric A shape conforming to the mathematical properties of lines, angles, and curves.

Hereditary Biological characteristics transmitted from one generation to the next.

Internet Large, international computer network linking millions of users worldwide. The Internet is used for communication and for obtaining information on almost any subject.

Microchip A tiny silicon wafer containing millions of microscopic electronic components in an integrated circuit. Microchips or microprocessors are the "brains" of computers.

Nerve Any of the cordlike bundles of fibers made up of neurons through which sensory stimuli and motor (movement) impulses pass between the brain or other parts of the central nervous system and the body.

Neurons Any of the impulse-conducting cells that constitute the brain, spinal column, and nerves.

Polarity A positive or negative electrical state, or the alignment of a magnetic field north or south.

Radioactive Matter that spontaneously emits energy and subatomic particles.

Semiconductor Any of a class of crystalline solids intermediate in electrical conductivity between a conductor and an insulator. Semiconductors are used to control an electric current.

Software Instructions that tell a computer what to do, comprising all the programs, procedures, and routines associated with its operation.

Solvent A substance that breaks down or dissolves another substance.

Toxin Any substance poisonous to an organism. The term is sometimes restricted to poisons produced by living organisms (biotoxins).

Vaccine Therapeutic material containing weakened antigens which, when administered to a patient, stimulates immunity and protects against infection.

Wave A progressive transfer of energy from one point to another in a medium, for example, air or water.

Waveband A range of wavelengths occupied by transmissions of a particular type, for example, broadcasting transmissions.

Wavelength The distance between one point on a wave to exactly the same point on the next wave cycle.

Index

Page numbers in **bold** refer to main articles; those in *italics* refer to illustrations.